Grammar, Punctuation & Spelling Activity Book

for ages 7-8

This CGP book is bursting with fun activities to build up children's skills and confidence.

It's ideal for extra practice to reinforce what they're learning in primary school. Enjoy!

Published by CGP

Editors:

Rachel Craig-McFeely, Catherine Heygate, Katya Parkes, Rebecca Russell

With thanks to Eleanor Claringbold and Alison Griffin for the proofreading.

With thanks to Jan Greenway for the copyright research.

ISBN: 978 1 78908 522 8

Printed by Elanders Ltd, Newcastle upon Tyne.
Images throughout the book from www.edu-clips.com
Cover design concept by emc design ltd.

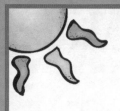

Contents

Nouns and adjectives	2
Articles	4
Verbs with 'have'	6
Adverbs	8
Sentences	10
Clauses	12
Puzzle: Super spies	14
Co-ordinating conjunctions	16
Subordinating conjunctions	18
Prepositions	20
Direct speech	22
Suffixes	24
Homophones	26
Answers	28

Nouns and adjectives

How It Works

Nouns are words that name things. Adjectives are words that describe nouns.

the wooden boat

↑ adjective   ↑ noun

Proper nouns are names for particular people, places or things. They always have a capital letter.

Friday
Manchester Simon

Now Try These

1. Draw lines to match each word to its word type.

Lucas

biscuit

noun

friend

friendly

strong

goat

adjective

butterfly

Italy

honest

tall

busy

2. Underline the words in the sentences below that should have a capital letter.

Our neighbour, mrs jones, was late because her car broke down.

I always sit with omar and susan on the school bus.

On saturday, we decided to cycle to glasgow.

My aunt and uncle are going to sail to america in august.

3. Use the words below to complete the sentences. In the white boxes, write whether each word is a noun or an adjective.

| teacher | hungry | puppy | new |

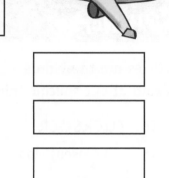

The .... barked loudly at the postman.

Yosef was .... , so he had a snack.

I have already lost one of my .... socks.

Our .... gave us some maths homework.

4. Choose an adjective to describe each picture below.

the .... bus   the .... boat   the ....
hot air balloon

An Extra Challenge

In the box, there are some nouns and some adjectives. Circle the nouns and underline the adjectives. Can you use them to describe the picture below?

helmet   green
road

tree   long
stripy

t-shirt

happy   red
boy

How did you get on? Did you steer your way to success?

3

Articles

Articles are the words 'a', 'an' and 'the'. They go before nouns. Use 'the' when talking about specific things and 'a' or 'an' when talking about general things.

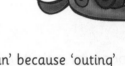

the rucksack
This means a particular rucksack.

a rucksack
This means any rucksack.

When the noun starts with a consonant sound, use 'a'.
Use 'an' when the noun starts with a vowel sound.

a tent
This is 'a' because 'tent' starts with a consonant sound.

an outing
This is 'an' because 'outing' starts with a vowel sound.

Now Try These

1. Circle the article in each sentence below.

I'm going to have an adventure.

I have a cosy sleeping bag.

We put up the tent.

I'm going to catch a fish.

2. Circle the right article in each sentence below.

I chose **a / an** orange and Eric decided to have a banana.

They watched **a / an** squirrel climb to the top of the tree.

Gillian was quite surprised to see **a / an** elephant in the park.

After school, we went to see **a / an** film at the cinema.

Obafemi swapped his jam tart for **a / an** chocolate biscuit.

3. Draw lines to match each sentence with the missing article.

My little brother is
afraid of ...... dark.

My boots are too small
so I need ...... new pair.

The badger keeps sneezing
— I think it has ...... cold.

Have you ever seen
such ...... unusual hat?

We had ...... exciting trip
to the science museum.

It was sunny, so we
went to ...... seaside.

4. Read the passage and cross out any incorrect articles. Write the
correct article above it. The first one has been done for you.

Tina and Jake had _the_ ~~a~~ best time when they went camping in **the** woods.

They spent hours exploring **the** forest. In **a** middle of **the** woods, they

found **an** huge river. They watched **a** otter hop out of **a** water and run

into **the** bushes. **The** few hours later, they toasted **a** entire bag

of marshmallows and ate them around **the** camp fire.

An Extra Challenge

How many different things can you spot in the picture below?
Should you use 'a' or 'an' for each one?

Are you an articles expert or do
you need a bit more practice?

5

Verbs with 'have'

How It Works

You can use the present tense form of 'to have' to talk about things that happened recently.

Ben has watched **the match.**

The present tense form of 'to have' comes first...

...then the past tense form of the main verb.

The past tense forms of some verbs are different when you use 'to have'.

She has thrown **the ball.**

not 'has threw'

We have chosen **a team.**

not 'have chose'

Now Try These

1. Draw lines to show which sentences use the present tense form of 'to have' and which ones do not.

He has scored a goal.

I have dropped my cricket bat.

Morag swung her hockey stick.

Amala had played basketball.

We ran across the pitch.

They have won the game.

2. Circle the right form of the verb to complete each sentence.

I have **wrote / written** a story about a magic teapot.

Tomasz has **done / did** all of his English homework.

Sam and Alex have **seen / saw** this film three times already.

The tallest tree in the park has **fell / fallen** over.

6

3. Use the present tense form of 'to have' and the right form of the verb in the box to complete each sentence.

work — Harry .... on his bowling.

visit — We .... our new school.

take — Mum .... James to tennis.

forget — I .... where I put my shoes.

eat — Greg and Rosie .... all the peas.

4. Rewrite these sentences using the present tense form of 'to have'.

Isha went to volleyball practice.

....

I drank some apple juice.

....

An Extra Challenge

Ben and Mia are great at football, but they're not so good at using verbs with 'have'. How many mistakes can you spot in their conversation? Can you correct them all?

Hi! I'm Ben. I has joined your team.

Hi! Have you played football before?

My mum have been a footballer for years. I has played with her a lot.

Great! We're a good team. We have beated every other team in the area.

Have you got the hang of verbs with 'have'? Give yourself a tick.

Adverbs

How It Works

Adverbs are words that describe verbs. They can tell you how a verb is done.

She paints messily.

← Adverbs often end with '-ly'.

Adverbs can also tell you when or where a verb is done.

I will paint a picture later.

This tells you when.

He is painting outside.

This tells you where.

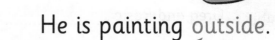

Now Try These

1. Circle the words below that are adverbs.

 often

 white

 tree

 rarely

 never

 horse

 sadly

 tall

 inside

 quickly

 write

 smooth

2. Underline the adverb in each sentence below.

Tanya always enjoys her art lessons.

The puppy barked happily and wagged its tail.

The children stared hungrily at the chocolate cake.

Dinesh carried his new toys upstairs.

3. Circle the right adverb to complete each sentence below.

Our art teacher only lets us use modelling clay **occasionally** / **soon**.

The vase he made for me was decorated **sometimes** / **beautifully**.

I was walking **soon** / **backwards** when I tripped over the frog.

Mike wasn't **occasionally** / **here** when Uncle Callum came to visit.

Mum **backwards** / **sometimes** lets us stay up late on Friday night.

4. Use the adverbs in the box to complete the sentences below.
Make sure you only use each adverb once.

| afterwards | forward | loudly | usually |

Grandad and I .... do some drawing on Saturday afternoons.

I rolled the dice and moved my counter .... five places.

Marie had a long nap — .... she felt wide awake.

We sang .... so that everyone in the hall could hear us.

An Extra Challenge

How many adverbs can you find on the easel?
Can you add them all to the instructions below?

- Pour the blue paint into a bowl.

- Add the red paint.

- Mix them together.

- Add white paint until
the mixture turns mauve.

gradually

slowly

most

firstly

quick

gentle

finally

next

thick

bright

carefully

Are you absolutely ace at using
adverbs? Give yourself a tick.

Sentences

There are different types of sentences.
Statements are sentences that give information.

He is wearing a coat.

Questions ask something and always end with a question mark.

Is he wearing a coat?

Exclamations show strong feelings.
They usually end with an exclamation mark.

Exclamations start with 'what' or 'how' and contain a verb.

What a big tornado that is!

Commands give instructions or orders.

Get out of that puddle.

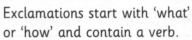

Now Try These

1. Each sentence below is either a statement, a question or an exclamation.
   Draw a line to match each one to the punctuation mark it should end with.

Did you see that rainbow

Autumn is my favourite season

What an amazing thunderstorm that was

How messy this room is

You should always wear sun cream

Where is Kat going skiing this year

2. Rearrange the words in these statements to turn them into questions.

It is Monday today.  .... Monday today?

Jessie is moving house. ➡ .... moving house?

Oscar was really excited. ➡ .... really excited?

He has seen the film. ➡ .... seen the film?

3. Read the sentences below. Can you circle
the commands and underline the statements?

Check the weather forecast before you go.

June put on her
new trainers.

Put your waterproof
jacket on, Sanjeet.

You should come
sledging with us.

They must take their lunch with them.

An Extra Challenge

Look at the two scenes below. For each one, write a statement, a command,
a question and an exclamation that someone in the scene might say.

Are sentences making sense?
Give yourself a tick.

Clauses

How It Works

Sentences are made up of groups of words called clauses.

They ordered two pizzas before I arrived.

This is a main clause — it would make sense as a separate sentence.

This is a subordinate clause — it adds extra information to the sentence, but it doesn't make sense on its own.

Now Try These

1. Draw lines to show whether the clauses below are main or subordinate clauses.

I love cake

he made dinner

while she waited

before we eat

you don't eat meat

if you're hungry

main clauses

subordinate clauses

2. Use a subordinate clause from Question 1 to complete each of these sentences.

You should wash your hands ....

.... , there are some pancakes left.

Penny ate an apple ....

3. Underline the subordinate clause in each of these sentences.

If you don't hurry up, we'll miss our train.

You have to finish tidying up before you can go out.

Julian made lunch while his sister played in the garden.

After he cleaned the kitchen, Liam made some biscuits.

4. Complete each of these sentences by adding your own main clause.

....

....

.... while we were eating dinner.

After she added the tomato sauce, ...

....

....

An Extra Challenge

Can you complete the sentences below to describe what's happening in the picture?
Each sentence needs to have a main clause and a subordinate clause.

Do you feel like a clever clogs
when it comes to clauses?

Super spies

This team of secret agents is looking for the hidden entrance to the evil organisation, Bad Guys Inc., and they need your help. Answer each question to collect the letters which will reveal the location of the entrance.

1. Which of these examples uses direct speech correctly?

- "Hide! Someone's coming"! — O

- "pass me my night-vision goggles," she said. — B

- "I can't see a thing," he muttered. — (T)

2. True or false? Co-ordinating conjunctions join a main clause to a subordinate clause.

- True — O

- False — H

3. Which of these words is spelt correctly?

- basicly — A

- terrifically — E

- angryly — I

4. Which of these examples uses a verb with 'have' correctly?

- we have went — L

- she has wrote — B

- I have done — O

5. Identify the sentence where the adverb has been underlined.

- We <u>sometimes</u> go on undercover missions. — L

- <u>Being</u> a secret agent is hard work. — I

- I catch <u>bad</u> guys every day. — U

14

6. Which of these groups of words is all prepositions?

- on, in, until — D

- inside, never, always — G

- but, and, yet — P

7. True or false? Adjectives always describe verbs.

- True — J

- False — B

8. Identify the sentence where the subordinate clause has been underlined.

- We won't stop <u>until we catch them</u>. — A

- If they escape, <u>we will find them</u>. — U

9. Which sentence uses articles correctly?

- We are the best team of secret agents in a world. — S

- We're getting close to finding the hidden entrance. — R

- It takes years of training to become a agent. — L

10. Which of these sentences is a command?

- You've been caught. — F

- Put your hands up. — N

- We're taking you to jail. — M

TOP SECRET LOCATION

1 T	2	3

4	5	6

7	8	9	10

Co-ordinating conjunctions

How It Works

Conjunctions are words or phrases that join two parts of a sentence together. Co-ordinating conjunctions join two main clauses.

Mum lit the candles and Samira blew them out.

first main clause   conjunction   second main clause

These words are all co-ordinating conjunctions:

For And Nor But Or Yet So

You can remember them as the FANBOYS conjunctions.

Now Try These

1. Underline the co-ordinating conjunction in each of these sentences.

I'm excited for it's my birthday tomorrow.

I'm having a party and I have invited all of my friends.

We have lots of balloons but I forgot to buy streamers.

We might play musical chairs or we might play pass-the-parcel.

2. Draw lines to join the two parts of these sentences using the right conjunction.

Do you like this hat   **and**   it wasn't windy enough.

He wanted to fly his kite   **so**   I swam in the sea.

I went to the beach   **or**   she went to the doctor.

Gemma didn't feel well   **but**   do you prefer that one?

3. Circle the right co-ordinating conjunction in each sentence below.

We will have cupcakes **and** / **nor** we will have ice cream.

Fiona doesn't like pink **for** / **nor** does she like princesses.

Did you have a chocolate cake **or** / **so** did you have a vanilla one?

Syed didn't cycle to the park **but** / **for** he couldn't find his bike.

4. Join each pair of sentences together using one of the conjunctions below. Make sure you only use each conjunction once.

and   yet   so

I set five alarms. I still overslept.

....

Marcus was tired. He had a rest.

....

We have a rabbit. We have four mice.

....

An Extra Challenge

Naya has written an invitation for her birthday party but she's got some conjunctions wrong. How many mistakes can you spot? Can you correct them all?

<u>Naya's 8th Birthday Party</u>

The party starts at 3 pm but it will finish at 5.30 pm.

You can come alone yet you can bring some friends with you.

It's a fancy dress party nor make sure you dress up!

Are you a fan of the FANBOYS conjunctions? Tick a box.

Subordinating conjunctions

How It Works

Subordinating conjunctions join a subordinate clause to a main clause.

We went to the beach (because) it was a beautiful day.

main clause →   subordinating conjunction   subordinate clause

Sometimes, a subordinating conjunction comes at the start of a sentence.

(Although) it was cold, we swam in the sea.

subordinating conjunction   subordinate clause   main clause

Now Try These

1. Circle the words that can be subordinating conjunctions.

 since

 gone

 because

 he

 ran

 and

 nor

 if

2. Underline the subordinating conjunction in each sentence.

I ordered a strawberry milkshake because it's my favourite.

Anna and Ella surfed until it was time for lunch.

There were hundreds of people wherever we looked.

If it stays dry, we'll play football in the park later.

After she went swimming, Aisha played catch with her mum.

3. Circle the right subordinating conjunction in each sentence below.

Because / Until Isaiah couldn't swim, a lifeguard had to save him.

Emilia drew a picture **if / while** Jay watched TV.

I brush my teeth **before / although** I go to bed.

Although / When Jamie went diving, he saw a shark.

4. Draw lines to join the clauses below using the right subordinating conjunction.

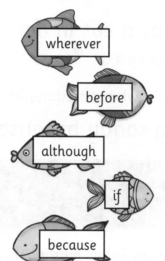

Let's buy some ice lollies   wherever   we get the car sandy.

Ed used to take his teddy   before   he went.

Lottie was upset   although   I prefer sweets.

The seats will be scratchy   if   the queue gets too long.

I like chocolate   because   she lost her surfboard.

An Extra Challenge

Molly and Keone ran onto the sand. Since it was such a hot day, they went straight into the sea. They splashed around in the water until they started to feel cooler. Keone wanted to play catch but he realised his beach ball had blown away. While Molly waited for him to find it, she started to plan a giant sand castle.

Can you spot all the subordinating conjunctions in this story?

Now add two more sentences to the end of the story. Try to use a subordinating conjunction in each sentence.

Are you cracking at conjunctions? Tick a box.

How It Works

Prepositions are words that tell you where things are or when things happen, in relation to one another.

They found the tortoise under the sink.

This tells you <u>where</u> the tortoise was in relation to the sink.

We're going to adopt a cat in January.

This tells you <u>when</u> they're adopting a cat.

Prepositions can also help explain why something happens.

I can't walk the dog today because of the storm.

Now Try These

1. Can you complete the sentences below so that they describe the picture?
   Try to use a different preposition in each sentence.

The cat is .... the sofa.   The bird is .... the window.

The dog is .... his bed.   The mouse is .... the table.

The snake is .... the sofa.   The frog is .... the mouse.

2. Circle the right preposition in each sentence below.

Jennifer always feeds her rats **before / until** bed.

Kylie is going **of / to** the ice-skating rink.

The game was cancelled **due to / behind** the rain.

They live **to / on** a farm and take care of sick llamas.

3. Use the prepositions in the box to complete the sentences below. Make sure you only use each preposition once.

inside	under	because of	during

Our new cat, Mittens, only sleeps .... the day.

Buster is frightened .... the fireworks.

Hamsters can fit lots of food .... their cheeks.

My sister hides her sweets .... her bed.

An Extra Challenge

Li is trying to get to the vet but someone has muddled up the prepositions in the directions. Help him by swapping the prepositions around so that the directions make sense.

Turn right just **under** you reach the bank. Walk **before** the bridge. Keep walking **opposite** you get to the supermarket. Turn left. The vet's is **in** the bakery. You will see the big sign hanging **until** the window.

Queue here

How did you get on with these pre-paw-sitions? Tick a box.

Direct speech

How It Works

Direct speech means the actual words that someone says.
Inverted commas (or speech marks) go at the start and end of direct speech.

"I'm off to work," said Mum.

inverted commas   inverted commas

The first word of direct speech usually has a capital letter.
Direct speech always ends with a punctuation mark.

"What do you want to be when you grow up?"

Now Try These

1. Can you put inverted commas in the right places in these sentences?
   The first one has been done for you.

   "☐ Look how fast I can run! " ☐ he said ☐ excitedly. ☐

   ☐ Lydia asked, ☐ How did you ☐ become a dinosaur expert? ☐

   ☐ You would make ☐ a good teacher, ☐ said ☐ my stepmum.

   ☐ I'm a fully qualified nurse, ☐ said Caleb ☐ proudly. ☐

2. Circle the word that should have a capital letter in each sentence.

   "that film was so scary," said my big brother.

   Olivia said, "it's my job to fix roads."

   Peter asked, "how long have you been a scientist for?"

   "we have to go home for dinner," said Farah.

   My dad asked, "would you like pancakes or waffles?"

3. Tick the sentences that use direct speech correctly.

"Nathan said, My dad used to be a butcher."

"I was really pleased when I won the prize," Mia said.

"do you enjoy being in the army?" Demi asked.

"Toby just got fired! gasped Anwar."

"We're going to visit my grandparents this week," he said.

"Have you thought about being an astronaut?" she asked.

4. Can you rewrite the incorrect sentences from Question 3 without any mistakes?

....

....

....

An Extra Challenge

Can you write out what each person is saying as direct speech?
You'll need to use speech marks and the correct punctuation.

I love my job.

May

How can I help you?

Dr Gray

What a great show that was!

Joe

Have you finished your homework?

Mr Khan

What would you say about your direct speech skills? Tick a box.

Suffixes

A suffix is a letter or group of letters that can be added to the end of a root word to make a new word.

quick ➕ er ➡ quicker

↑ root word   ↑ suffix   ↑ new word

Sometimes the spelling of the root word changes when a suffix is added.

sad ➕ ness ➡ sadness   happy ➕ ness ➡ happiness

The spelling of the root word 'sad' doesn't change when '-ness' is added...   ...but the spelling of the root word 'happy' does.

Now Try These

1. Circle the words below that are spelt wrong.
   Can you write them out without any mistakes?

flying

smaler

furyous

....

excitment

spookyness

relaxation

....

2. Circle the right spelling of each word to complete the sentences below.

The witch gave the potion a **carful** / **careful** stir.

I can run so much **faster** / **fastter** than you.

Will and his brother had an **arguement** / **argument**.

The burst football was **usless** / **useless**.

The spider **hurryed** / **hurried** across the floor.

3. Can you add these suffixes to the root words?

magical ly ➡ ....

imagine ➕ ation ➡ ....

easy ➕ est ➡ ....

poison ➕ ous ➡ ....

An Extra Challenge

Lea is practising her spells. Can you help her transform these root words and suffixes into new words? See how many different words you can make. Remember — the spelling of the root words may change when you add a suffix.

sad   ly

mix   er

like   ed

wait   ing

How many new words did you make?

0 - 4 — Keep going! Lea needs your help.
5 - 8 — Great work! Can you find a few more?
9 + — Amazing! Thanks to you, Lea's a pro.

Satisfied with suffixes? Tick a box to show how you got on.

25

Homophones

How It Works

Homophones are words that sound the same, but have different meanings and spellings.

flower

A flower is part of a plant.

 flour

Flour is an ingredient in cakes and bread.

Now Try These

1. Write the homophone that matches each picture.

   plain

   ....

   night

   ....

   bare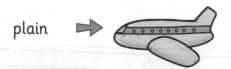

   ....

   pair

   ....

   meddle

   ....

   right

   ....

2. Circle the right homophone to complete each sentence below.

   Let's plant the tree **here** / **hear**.

   My sister turned **ate** / **eight** years old today.

   I hope the storm won't **affect** / **effect** our trip.

3. Complete each sentence by adding the right homophone from the box.

buy / bye   He needs to .... some new shoes.

bury / berry   My dog loves to .... his toys in the garden.

no / know   We .... the way to school.

Hour / Our   .... garden is small but it's really pretty.

rain / reign   It looks like it's going to .... today.

4. Circle the two sentences that use the wrong homophone.
Can you rewrite them without any mistakes?

Where are my
gardening gloves?

They ate all there sweets.

There aren't any sweets left.

I always where
gardening gloves.

....

....

An Extra Challenge

Can you think of a homophone for each word in the picture?
See if you can use each pair of homophones in a sentence.

weather   scene   maid   mist   weight

Do you always write the right
homophone? Tick a box.

27

Answers

Pages 2-3 — Nouns and adjectives

1. nouns: Lucas, friend, butterfly, biscuit, goat, Italy
   adjectives: strong, honest, tall, friendly, busy

2. You should have underlined: mrs, jones, omar, susan, saturday, glasgow, america, august

3. The <u>puppy</u> barked loudly at the postman. — noun
   Yosef was <u>hungry</u>, so he had a snack. — adjective
   I have already lost one of my <u>new</u> socks. — adjective
   Our <u>teacher</u> gave us some maths homework. — noun

4. Any sensible answers, e.g. the crowded bus / the fast boat / the colourful hot air balloon

   An Extra Challenge

   nouns: road, helmet, tree, t-shirt, boy
   adjectives: green, stripy, long, happy, red
   Any sensible descriptions, e.g. a long road / a red helmet / a green tree / a stripy t-shirt / a happy boy

Pages 4-5 — Articles

1. I'm going to have <u>an</u> adventure.
   I have <u>a</u> cosy sleeping bag.
   We put up <u>the</u> tent.
   I'm going to catch <u>a</u> fish.

2. I chose <u>an</u> orange and Eric decided to have a banana.
   They watched <u>a</u> squirrel climb to the top of the tree.
   Gillian was quite surprised to see <u>an</u> elephant in the park.
   After school, we went to see <u>a</u> film at the cinema.
   Obafemi swapped his jam tart for <u>a</u> chocolate biscuit.

3. My little brother is afraid of <u>the</u> dark.
   The badger keeps sneezing — I think it has <u>a</u> cold.
   We had <u>an</u> exciting trip to the science museum.
   My boots are too small so I need <u>a</u> new pair.
   Have you ever seen such <u>an</u> unusual hat?
   It was sunny, so we went to <u>the</u> seaside.

4. Tina and Jake had the best time when they went camping in the woods. They spent hours exploring the forest. In <u>the</u> middle of the woods, they found <u>a</u> huge river. They watched <u>an</u> otter hop out of <u>the</u> water and run into the bushes. <u>A</u> few hours later, they toasted <u>an</u> entire bag of marshmallows and ate them around the camp fire.

   An Extra Challenge

   Any sensible answers, e.g. a tree, a girl, a boy, an owl, an ant, a rabbit, an acorn, a fire, a log, a boot, a t-shirt

Pages 6-7 — Verbs with 'have'

1. tick: He has scored a goal. / I have dropped my cricket bat. / They have won the game.
   cross: Morag swung her hockey stick. / Amala had played basketball. / We ran across the pitch.

2. I have <u>written</u> a story about a magic teapot.
   Tomasz has <u>done</u> all of his English homework.
   Sam and Alex have <u>seen</u> this film three times already.
   The tallest tree in the park has <u>fallen</u> over.

3. Harry <u>has worked</u> on his bowling.
   We <u>have visited</u> our new school.
   Mum <u>has taken</u> James to tennis.
   I <u>have forgotten</u> where I put my shoes.
   Greg and Rosie <u>have eaten</u> all the peas.

4. Isha has gone to volleyball practice.
   I have drunk some apple juice.

   An Extra Challenge

   Hi! I'm Ben. I <u>have</u> joined your team.
   Hi! Have you played football before?
   My mum <u>has</u> been a footballer for years. I <u>have</u> played with her a lot.
   Great! We're a good team. We have <u>beaten</u> every other team in the area.

Pages 8-9 — Adverbs

1. You should have circled: often, rarely, never, sadly, inside, quickly

2. You should have underlined: always, happily, hungrily, upstairs

3. Our art teacher only lets us use modelling clay <u>occasionally</u>.
   The vase he made for me was decorated <u>beautifully</u>.
   I was walking <u>backwards</u> when I tripped over the frog.
   Mike wasn't <u>here</u> when Uncle Callum came to visit.
   Mum <u>sometimes</u> lets us stay up late on Friday night.

4. Grandad and I <u>usually</u> do some drawing on Saturday afternoons.
   I rolled the dice and moved my counter <u>forward</u> five places.
   Marie had a long nap — <u>afterwards</u> she felt wide awake.
   We sang <u>loudly</u> so that everyone in the hall could hear us.

   An Extra Challenge

   You should have circled: gradually, slowly, firstly, finally, next, carefully

   Any sensible answer, e.g. <u>Firstly</u>, pour the blue paint <u>carefully</u> into a bowl. <u>Next</u>, add the red paint. <u>Slowly</u> mix them together. <u>Finally</u>, add white paint <u>gradually</u> until the mixture turns mauve.

Pages 10-11 — Sentences

1. exclamation mark: What an amazing thunderstorm that was / How messy this room is
   question mark: Did you see that rainbow / Where is Kat going skiing this year

Answers

full stop: Autumn is my favourite season / You should always wear sun cream

2. <u>Is it</u> Monday today?
<u>Is Jessie</u> moving house?
<u>Was Oscar</u> really excited?
<u>Has he</u> seen the film?

3. commands: Check the weather forecast before you go. / Put your waterproof jacket on, Sanjeet.
statements: June put on her new trainers. / You should come sledging with us. / They must take their lunch with them.

An Extra Challenge

Any sensible sentences for each picture, e.g.
statement: I wish I'd brought a scarf.
command: Stop throwing snowballs at me.
question: Do you want to build a snowman with me?
exclamation: How cold it is out here!

Pages 12-13 — Clauses

1. main clauses: I love cake / he made dinner / you don't eat meat
subordinate clauses: before we eat / while she waited / if you're hungry

2. You should wash your hands <u>before we eat</u>.
<u>If you're hungry</u>, there are some pancakes left.
Penny ate an apple <u>while she waited</u>.

3. <u>If you don't hurry up</u>, we'll miss our train.
You have to finish tidying up <u>before you can go out</u>.
Julian made lunch <u>while his sister played in the garden</u>.
<u>After he cleaned the kitchen</u>, Liam made some biscuits.

4. Any sensible answers, e.g. <u>My little sister threw peas all over the table</u> while we were eating dinner.
After she added the tomato sauce, <u>she put cheese and ham on her pizza</u>.

An Extra Challenge

Any sensible sentences that contain both a main and a subordinate clause, e.g. <u>When I found out the tomato could talk</u>, I decided to take it home.

Pages 14-15 — Super spies

1. "I can't see a thing," he muttered. — T
2. False — H
3. terrifically — E
4. I have done — O
5. We <u>sometimes</u> go on undercover missions. — L
6. on, in, until — D
7. False — B
8. We won't stop <u>until we catch them</u>. — A

9. We're getting close to finding the hidden entrance. — R
10. Put your hands up. — N

TOP SECRET LOCATION: THE OLD BARN

Pages 16-17 — Co-ordinating conjunctions

1. You should have underlined: for, and, but, or

2. Do you like this hat <u>or</u> do you prefer that one?
He wanted to fly his kite <u>but</u> it wasn't windy enough.
I went to the beach <u>and</u> I swam in the sea.
Gemma didn't feel well <u>so</u> she went to the doctor.

3. We will have cupcakes <u>and</u> we will have ice cream.
Fiona doesn't like pink <u>nor</u> does she like princesses.
Did you have a chocolate cake <u>or</u> did you have a vanilla one?
Syed didn't cycle to the park <u>for</u> he couldn't find his bike.

4. I set five alarms <u>yet</u> I still overslept.
Marcus was tired <u>so</u> he had a rest.
We have a rabbit <u>and</u> we have four mice.

An Extra Challenge

<u>Naya's 8th Birthday Party</u>
The party starts at 3 pm <u>and</u> it will finish at 5.30 pm.
You can come alone <u>or</u> you can bring some friends with you.
It's a fancy dress party <u>so</u> make sure you dress up!

Pages 18-19 — Subordinating conjunctions

1. You should have circled: since, because, if

2. You should have underlined: because, until, wherever, If, After

3. <u>Because</u> Isaiah couldn't swim, a lifeguard had to save him.
Emilia drew a picture <u>while</u> Jay watched TV.
I brush my teeth <u>before</u> I go to bed.
<u>When</u> Jamie went diving, he saw a shark.

4. Let's buy some ice lollies <u>before</u> the queue gets too long.
Ed used to take his teddy <u>wherever</u> he went.
Lottie was upset <u>because</u> she lost her surfboard.
The seats will be scratchy <u>if</u> we get the car sandy.
I like chocolate <u>although</u> I prefer sweets.

An Extra Challenge

You should have underlined: Since, until, While

Any sensible sentences that include subordinating conjunctions, e.g. <u>Once</u> Keone got back, they played catch together for a long time. <u>When</u> Molly's stomach started rumbling, they stopped playing and ran up the beach to get lunch.

Answers

Pages 20-21 — Prepositions

1. Any sensible answers, e.g.
   The cat is <u>on</u> the sofa.
   The dog is <u>next to</u> his bed.
   The snake is <u>behind</u> the sofa.
   The bird is <u>outside</u> the window.
   The mouse is <u>under</u> the table.
   The frog is <u>above</u> the mouse.

2. Jennifer always feeds her rats <u>before</u> bed.
   Kylie is going <u>to</u> the ice-skating rink.
   The game was cancelled <u>due to</u> the rain.
   They live <u>on</u> a farm and take care of sick llamas.

3. Our new cat, Mittens, only sleeps <u>during</u> the day.
   Buster is frightened <u>because of</u> the fireworks.
   Hamsters can fit lots of food <u>inside</u> their cheeks.
   My sister hides her sweets <u>under</u> her bed.

An Extra Challenge

Turn right just <u>before</u> you reach the bank. Walk <u>under</u> the bridge. Keep walking <u>until</u> you get to the supermarket. Turn left. The vet's is <u>opposite</u> the bakery. You will see the big sign hanging <u>in</u> the window.

Pages 22-23 — Direct speech

1. Lydia asked, <u>"</u>How did you become a dinosaur expert?<u>"</u>
   <u>"</u>You would make a good teacher,<u>"</u> said my stepmum.
   <u>"</u>I'm a fully qualified nurse,<u>"</u> said Caleb proudly.

2. "<u>that</u> film was so scary," said my big brother.
   Olivia said, "<u>it's</u> my job to fix roads."
   Peter asked, "<u>how</u> long have you been a scientist for?"
   "<u>we</u> have to go home for dinner," said Farah.
   My dad asked, "<u>would</u> you like pancakes or waffles?"

3. You should have ticked:
   "I was really pleased when I won the prize," Mia said.
   "We're going to visit my grandparents this week," he said.
   "Have you thought about being an astronaut?" she asked.

4. Nathan said, <u>"</u>My dad used to be a butcher."
   "<u>D</u>o you enjoy being in the army?" Demi asked.
   "Toby just got fired!<u>"</u> gasped Anwar.

An Extra Challenge

Any answers where the direct speech is punctuated correctly, e.g.
May said, "I love my job."
"How can I help you?" asked Dr Gray.
Joe said, "What a great show that was!"
"Have you finished your homework?" asked Mr Khan.

Pages 24-25 — Suffixes

1. The correct spellings are: smal<u>l</u>er, fur<u>i</u>ous, excit<u>e</u>ment, spook<u>i</u>ness.

2. The witch gave the potion a <u>careful</u> stir.
   I can run so much <u>faster</u> than you.
   Will and his brother had an <u>argument</u>.
   The burst football was <u>useless</u>.
   The spider <u>hurried</u> across the floor.

3. magically, imagination, easiest, poisonous

An Extra Challenge

Any answers which are spelt correctly, e.g. sadly, sadder, mixer, mixed, mixing, likely, liked, liking, waiter, waited, waiting

Pages 26-27 — Homophones

1. plain — plane / bare — bear / meddle — medal / night — knight / pair — pear / right — write

2. Let's plant the tree <u>here</u>.
   My sister turned <u>eight</u> years old today.
   I hope the storm won't <u>affect</u> our trip.

3. He needs to <u>buy</u> some new shoes.
   My dog loves to <u>bury</u> his toys in the garden.
   We <u>know</u> the way to school.
   <u>Our</u> garden is small but it's really pretty.
   It looks like it's going to <u>rain</u> today.

4. You should have circled:
   They ate all <u>there</u> sweets.
   I always <u>where</u> gardening gloves.
   You should have written:
   They ate all <u>their</u> sweets.
   I always <u>wear</u> gardening gloves.

An Extra Challenge

Any sensible answers, e.g.
weather — whether
I wonder <u>whether</u> the <u>weather</u> will be hot tomorrow.
scene — seen
Have you <u>seen</u> the <u>scene</u> with the pirates?
maid — made
The <u>maid</u> <u>made</u> the bed.
mist — missed
They <u>missed</u> the fireworks because of the <u>mist</u>.
weight — wait
We had to <u>wait</u> a long time to find out the <u>weight</u> of the winning cauliflower.

BLUES IMPROVISATION COMPLETE B♭

JEFF HARRINGTON

Berklee Media

Associate Vice President: Dave Kusek
Director of Content: Debbie Cavalier
Business Manager: Jennifer Rassler

Berklee Press

Senior Writer/Editor: Jonathan Feist
Writer/Editor: Susan Gedutis
Production Manager: Shawn Girsberger

ISBN 0-634-01530-3

1140 Boylston Street
Boston, MA 02215-3693 USA
(617) 747-2146

Visit Berklee Press Online at
www.berkleepress.com

DISTRIBUTED BY

HAL•LEONARD®
CORPORATION
7777 W. BLUEMOUND RD. P.O. BOX 13819
MILWAUKEE, WISCONSIN 53213

Visit Hal Leonard Online at
www.halleonard.com

CD TRACK LISTING

Track*	Key	Style	Eighth-Note Feel	Pages
1	D	bop	swing	5, 28, 43, 70, 84, 96
2	G	bossa nova	even	29, 45, 71, 85
3	C	shuffle	swing	30, 47, 72, 86
4	F	funk	even	31, 49, 73, 87, 103
5	B♭	bop	swing	32, 51, 74, 88
6	E♭	bossa nova	even	33, 53, 75, 89
7	A♭	shuffle	swing	34, 55, 76, 90
8	C♯	funk	even	35, 57, 77, 91, 104
9	F♯	bop	swing	36, 59, 78, 92
10	B	Afro-Cuban	swing	37, 61, 79, 93
11	E	shuffle	swing	38, 63, 80, 94
12	A	bugaloo	even	39, 65, 81, 95
13	D	Latin	even	28, 43, 70, 84, 96
14	G	bop	swing	29, 45, 71, 85
15	C	half-time funk	even	30, 47, 72, 86, 105
16	F	New Orleans shuffle	swing	31, 49, 73, 87
17	B♭	Latin	even	32, 51, 74, 88
18	E♭	bop	swing	33, 53, 75, 89
19	A♭	funk	even	34, 55, 76, 90, 106
20	C♯	shuffle	swing	35, 57, 77, 91
21	F♯	Latin	even	36, 59, 78, 92
22	B	bop	swing	37, 61, 79, 93
23	E	funk shuffle	swing	38, 63, 80, 94
24	A	swing	swing	39, 65, 81, 95
25	TUNING NOTE: B			

*TRACKS 1–12: 8 choruses each at mm 106. TRACKS 13–24: 6 choruses each at mm 145.

CONTENTS

CD Track Listing ii

Acknowledgments iv

Introduction 1

Getting Started 5

Section One: Blues Scale Exercises 11

Section Two: Blues Scale One-Bar Ideas 24

Section Three: Blues Scale Solos Based on the Root .40

Section Four: Blues Scale Solos Based on the Sixth Degree 67

Section Five: Blues Scale Solos Based on the Root and the Sixth Degree 82

50 Blues Licks 96

Funk One-Bar Rhythms and Solos 101

Traditional Blues Songs 107

Blues Scales 113

45 Recorded Excerpts for Listening and Transcribing .114

15 Tunes That Are Predominantly Composed of the Blues Scale 120

Recommended Listening 121

ACKNOWLEDGMENTS

Special thanks to all of my teachers, especially Jerry Bergonzi and George Garzone, my students, and my mother for her expertise, love, and support.

Special thanks to the musicians who performed on the CD recording:
Steve Hunt: keyboards
Christian Fabian: acoustic and electric bass
Steve Michaud: drums

Recorded and mixed at The Kitchen, Chelmsford, MA, September 24 and 27, 1999
Recording engineer: Steve Hunt
Produced by Jeff Harrington

INTRODUCTION

ABOUT THE BLUES

Over the last century, the United States has given rise to three distinct styles of music: blues, jazz, and rock. No longer unique to the U.S., these styles have spread throughout the world. Each one has a long and colorful history, rich in substyles, remarkable recordings, and a lineage of brilliant artists.

The style of music known as blues dates back to the late 19th century and was born out of the African American experience. No one knows for sure exactly when it came to be. Delta blues, Chicago blues, Memphis blues, boogie woogie, jump blues, and rhythm & blues (r&b) are just some of the styles that have evolved over time. Funk, which is an outgrowth of rhythm & blues, incorporates several different styles of blues.

Jazz came along next, beginning in New Orleans around the turn of the century. Some early jazz was similar to the blues of that period. Dixieland, Chicago jazz, swing, bebop, bossa nova, free jazz, Afro-Cuban jazz, and fusion are various styles of jazz.

In the 1950s, r&b's sister, rock 'n' roll, was born. Sixties rock, British rock, punk, new wave, and alternative rock followed.

While the three major styles are basically quite different, they all share a common element, the 12-bar blues. In fact, they not only share it; the 12-bar blues is one of the most often played and, therefore, most important chord progressions in each of the three styles. To be an accomplished blues, jazz, or rock musician, mastery of the 12-bar blues is essential.

Despite its early origins, the 12-bar blues remains as much a part of American music and culture today as ever. For example, "Hound Dog," recorded in 1956 by Elvis Presley, is a 12-bar blues. So is "Frankie and Johnny," which was written in the late 1800s and became a New Orleans standard. Jazz genius Charlie Parker revolutionized the blues during the forties and fifties. Sixties rock bands such as the Beatles and Cream frequently included blues on their recordings, and Chicago blues artist B.B. King plays almost exclusively 12-bar blues. Pick up any current CD by a contemporary jazz artist such as Michael Brecker, Joshua Redman, Wynton Marsalis, Chick Corea, or John Scofield, and chances are it includes at least one blues.

JUST WHAT IS A BLUES, ANYWAY?

Is a blues sad? Is it happy? Is it slow or is it fast? The answer is yes, a blues can possess any of these qualities.

A blues is a song form. It is not to be confused with the style of music known as "the blues," which has been played by musicians such as B.B. King and Muddy Waters. It is a song form that is 12 bars in length with a set chord progression. This means that for each bar, there is a chord that a piano or guitar would play. The chords supply the harmony. There are many variations to a 12-bar blues chord progression. The 12 bars are usually divided up into three four-bar phrases. The following is a standard 12-bar blues chord progression in the key of C:

1st phrase: C7	F7	C7	C7
2nd phrase: F7	F7	C7	C7
3rd phrase: G7	F7	C7	C7

Here's the same progression with Roman numeral analysis:

1st phrase:	I7	IV7	I7	I7
2nd phrase:	IV7	IV7	I7	I7
3rd phrase:	V7	IV7	I7	I7

This is a common variation:

C7	F7	C7	C7
F7	F7	C7	A7
D–7	G7	C7	C7

Here it is with Roman numeral analysis:

I7	IV7	I7	I7
IV7	IV7	I7	V7/II
II–7	V7	I7	I7

In addition to these two progressions, the accompaniment on the CD includes others, in order to create variety and contrast.

Now, over these chords we have a melody. Improvising, or spontaneously creating a melodic solo line, over these chords is the focus of this book.

About This Book

This book is a guide to improvisation for the beginner. Its focus is on teaching several basic approaches to improvising a melodic line over a 12-bar blues. These approaches are fundamental to developing improvisational skill in jazz, Latin, fusion, blues, and rock.

The book is divided into five sections. The first section, Blues Scale Exercises, is designed to prepare you with the knowledge and technique necessary to improvise with this scale. The second section, Blues Scale One-Bar Ideas, features simple melodic fragments using only the blues scale. Third, Blues Scale Solos Based on the Root, are examples of entire solos over the 12-bar blues chord progression using only the blues scale. Fourth is Blues Scale Solos Based on the Sixth Degree. These solos also use the blues scale but have an entirely different melodic and harmonic flavor. The fifth section is Blues Scales Based on the Root and Sixth Degree. Combining the two scales creates a greater variety of moods and colors. Sections Two through Five can be played with the E♭, C, and bass clef versions of this book. Section Five is followed by additional rhythms and solos in a funk style.

The book also includes a lick compendium, a scale reference page, a list of recorded examples, recommended listening, traditional blues songs comprised entirely of blues scales, and a glossary of technical terms. The lick compendium can be played with the C, E♭, and bass clef versions of this book.

Each section includes a practice regimen, as well as step-by-step instructions on how to improvise and compose with the specific technique being taught.

In addition to learning to improvise over a blues, you will be learning to recognize the sound of the blues 12-bar chord progression by ear. Also, you will be developing in the areas of reading, technique, rhythmic syncopation, performing with a rhythm section, acquiring idiomatic melodic vocabulary, and composing. These are all essential skills you will need in order to master the art of improvisation.

The book focuses on getting certain scales, melodies, and chord progressions under your fingers and into your ears. The blues scale exercises and sample blues solos will serve as models for your own improvised solos. These models incorporate universal rhythmic and melodic vocabulary.

Each section of this book is written in 12 keys. The eventual goal is to feel comfortable playing in any key. This is part of being an accomplished and versatile musician. Naturally this takes time, but by beginning early, you will be on the right path from the start. In addition, many of the exercises and solos are transposed into several keys—some into all 12 keys. This will help you develop technical facility. By repeating the same melody in several keys, you will, over time, have memorized its sound, phrasing, and rhythm. Then, when you improvise to the same chord progression, the memorized solo or melodic fragment will serve as a template for your own ideas.

Once each piece is learned at tempo, you can then play it with the accompanying play-along CD. Next, you have the opportunity to improvise by imitating the sound and structure of the model. This is done by using the learned melodic material—a blues scale, for instance.

In conjunction with this method, you will begin memorizing and learning to hear the sound of the basic elements necessary for improvising. These include blues scales, blues scale melodies, and the 12-bar blues form.

Upon completion of this book, you should be able to improvise freely within the context of the material over a 12-bar blues chord progression, paving the way for further study and application.

The CD

The play-along CD includes two separate tracks for each key. The first is at mm 106 and the second is at mm 145. Once you have mastered the solos and your improvisation at mm 106, challenge yourself by gradually increasing your tempo to mm 145. When you're ready, try playing with the faster versions on the CD.

In addition, the left channel is only bass and drums, while the right channel is only paino and drums. By turning off the right channel, pianists or guitarists, for example, can play with only bass and drums. Similarly, by turning off the left channel, bass players can play with only piano and drums. Horn players may want to try playing with only bass and drums, a common instrumentation used by such players as Gerry Mulligan, John Coltrane, and Michael Brecker.

Also, several different rhythmic "feels" are represented. They include bebop, swing, shuffle, New Orleans shuffle, bossa nova, Afro-Cuban, half-time funk, and funk shuffle.

How Improvisation Works

Once a melody is memorized, we're able to play it by accessing the part of our brain (our "ear") that remembers its sound. We no longer need to recall the name and order of each pitch because we can play it intuitively.

At first, when we try to play a particular scale or melody not yet fully memorized, our mind tells us which note goes first, second, and so forth. But once our "ear" learns the sound of the scale or melody, it tells our fingers which note to play. We hear it and therefore, we can play it. This is a key element in improvising. Of course, knowledge of your instrument is a prerequisite, and the more mastery you have, the better.

Think of a song you know very well, "Happy Birthday," for example. Now sing the song. Next, try to play it on your instrument. Chances are you were fairly successful. This illustrates one of the fundamental principles in improvisation: being able to play material by "ear" enables you to play it without thinking. Once your ear knows it, then you should be able to sing it. Once you can sing it, then you're able to play it on your instrument.

This process is similar to how we learn languages. We speak our native tongue by ear, having picked it up as children through constant listening. The sounds (vowels, consonants, and inflections), words (and their meaning), and grammatical constructions were absorbed and memorized gradually through continuous exposure, so that we are able to express our thoughts as quickly as they occur to us.

Naturally, as you become involved in the process of learning to improvise, your ear will become quicker at picking up more and more complex material. This will enable you to absorb the sounds and vocabulary needed to express yourself fully.

In addition, the analytical mind plays a very important part in improvising. For example, the study and application of theory is an essential element in learning to improvise.

GETTING STARTED

The Rhythm Section

At this point, I'd like to explain a little about the roles of each instrument in the rhythm section. The rhythm section is comprised of piano and/or guitar, bass, and drums. Each instrument has a specific function.

The drums' primary job is to keep the beat. In swing 4/4 time, the hi-hat beats on the second and fourth beat of each measure while the ride cymbal plays a rhythm that brings out the quarter-note pulse (Ex. 1).

The bass usually plays quarter notes. This is called "walking bass." The pitches it plays are the notes of the chords as they are going by. Thus, its role is both to keep the beat and state the harmony.

The piano (or guitar) plays the chords with various rhythms. The rhythms may be syncopated or not. They may be short or sustained. Whatever combinations of rhythms the piano plays, they are intended to mesh with and complement the bass and drums. This is called "comping."

 Play Track 1 on the CD for each of the following exercises. Practice every day until you begin to hear clearly each instrument fulfilling its role.

1. First time: try to identify and isolate the sound of each instrument.

2. Second time: concentrate only on the drums and listen to the hi-hat on 2 and 4. Listen to the ride cymbal suggesting the quarter-note pulse.

3. Third time: focus on the bass "walking" quarter notes.

4. Fourth time: listen only to the piano "comping" and hear how it fits in with the bass and drums.

Hearing Where "1" Is

Now, before you play along with the accompanying CD, it's important to be able to hear where the downbeat (1) of each measure is. This will prevent you from getting lost and help you to create logical melodic ideas.

To develop ability in this area, practice the following exercises with CD Track 1:

1. Listen to the beginning audible count, "1–2–3–4," and as the music starts, count out loud 1–2–3–4, 1–2–3–4, and so on, along with the beat. The numbers should feel as if they naturally belong with the pulse of the music. Continue practicing until it feels comfortable.

2. Next, start the track somewhere in the middle and see if you can hear where 1 of each measure is. Try counting the beats (1–2–3–4). If you're not sure whether you're right or don't know where to start, go back and practice Step 1. It's simply a matter of trying it repeatedly until you get it.

Hearing the Form

As explained earlier, the blues is a 12-bar form. This means that after every 12 bars, the 12 bars repeat. When a jazz quartet performs a blues, it is not unusual for them to repeat the form as many as 20 or more times. One time through the 12-bar form is called a "chorus."

In order to improvise intelligently, it's necessary to know where you are in the form at all times. The following exercises will help you hear the beginning of the form each time it repeats.

1. Play Track 1. Start at the beginning and count through the 12-measure form. That is, count, "**1**–2–3–4, **2**–2–3–4, **3**–2–3–4, **4**–2–3–4," and so on. When you reach "**12**–2–3–4," start over. Continue for the length of the CD track. Following each twelfth bar, the chord progression repeats. There are eight choruses in Track 1. Repeat the entire process every day.

2. After a week or so, try listening without counting. Can you hear where the beginning of the 12-bar form is? If not, continue practicing these exercises daily until you can. Listen to the sound of the piano chords changing. Soon, you will be anticipating the sound of the next chord. Learning to do this is no secret. It's simply a matter of repetition.

3. Try putting the CD on as background music while you're washing dishes or riding in a car. Listen to it just before going to sleep and just after waking up. The more you listen, the better. This is called saturated listening, a process similar to the way in which you learned your own language.

Hearing the Phrasing

In music, a phrase is like a sentence. The end of a phrase is often marked by a longer note or rest (like a half note or half rest). The 12-bar form is divided into three four-bar phrases, or sentences. Bars 1–4 make up the first phrase. Bars 5–8 make up the second, and bars 9–12 make up the third. At the beginning of each phrase, there is an important and noticeable chord change.

Play Track 1 and while counting through the form, listen to the first, fifth, and ninth bars. Can you hear the chords change? Keep listening and before long you'll be anticipating the sound of these chords.

The Blues Scale

The blues scale is a six-note scale. When compared to a major scale, which is a seven-note scale, the blues scale is: 1, ♭3, 4, ♭5, 5, ♭7 (Ex. 2).

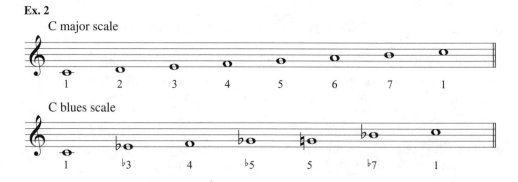

For example, the C major scale is: C, D, E, F, G, A, B, C. The C blues scale is: C, E♭, F, G♭, G, B♭, C.

This scale is used for improvisation in a wide variety of styles, including all types of jazz, blues, and rock. While we will be using this scale to improvise over a blues, it can be used for improvising over almost any chord progression.

R&B and pop players such as David Sanborn, Bob James, Larry Carlton, and Grover Washington, Jr. have used this scale frequently. This is also true for most rock players, such as Eric Clapton, Jimi Hendrix, Jeff Beck, and Steve Vai. Stanley Turrentine and Michael Brecker are just two of many jazz players who have chosen to shape their style with this scale. All of these great players' mastery of this six-note scale with regard to vocabulary, inflection, and technique enables them to create endless melodic and expressive variations.

The beauty of the blues scale is that it works over the entire 12-bar blues, and it is common to improvise with it in this way. However, the relationship between this scale and the blues chord progression is an unusual one. According to conventional music theory, the scale contains notes that would seem not to fit with the chords. In fact, there is no explanation for why these notes sound correct except that they've evolved this way and we've grown accustomed to the sound.

Practice Tips

The key to steady improvement is regular practice. Practicing every day (with an occasional day off) is essential for rapid progress. Once practicing becomes a daily routine, your day will feel incomplete without it. It's not unusual for musicians to feel guilty when they miss a day. This is actually a good thing: it helps to keep us motivated. It's called a "healthy obsession." Legend has it that the piano giant Vladimir Horowitz once said, "If I miss one day of practice, I notice it. If I miss two days of practice, the critics notice it. If I miss three days of practice, everyone notices it."

Beginners should practice a minimum of a half hour to an hour a day. Intermediate players should practice a minimum of one to three hours a day, and advanced players should practice a minimum of three to six hours a day. However, practicing any amount is better than not practicing at all.

When Charlie Parker was a teenager, he practiced 11 to 14 hours a day for four years. The neighbors asked his mother to move. John Coltrane would fall asleep with the saxophone in his mouth because he was so tired from long hours of practicing. A fan once complimented Artie Shaw on his wonderful playing, confessing that he had once played the clarinet but stopped because he lacked talent. Shaw reputedly replied, "Practice eight hours a day for ten years and come back and talk to me about talent." These examples illustrate that while these players were jazz masters of the highest order, they got there through dedication and hard work.

Divide your practice time into sections. If you have an hour and a half to practice, structure your time so that you touch on several different areas. For instance: 20 minutes on tone, 30 minutes on technical studies, 20 minutes on reading, and 20 minutes on improvisation. If you have less time, subtract five minutes from each category. Carry over fundamental concepts of tone, technique, intonation, and rhythm from one area to another. Identify your weaknesses and spend more time on those areas. Develop a routine and stick to it, adapting and adjusting it as needed. Organization is the key.

Don't worry about how fast you are progressing. Concentrate on improving your personal best and not on comparing yourself to some external standard. Have fun with the material and the joy of making music. Get involved with the process of learning and perfecting your music, and, most important, be patient with yourself.

Getting better is all about working hard on a consistent basis over time. Treat setbacks as merely bumps in the road and strike a balance between being self-critical and patting yourself on the back when you play something well. Both are equally important. Sometimes, frustration sets in when we try something new and different. Learn to recognize this and try to relax. At that point, it's often best to stop practicing and do something else for a few hours or even a day.

When practicing technique, warm up your fingers slowly and take occasional breaks. Think of how an athlete warms up for an event. Speed and accuracy are developed gradually over time. Keep your hands loose and relaxed, and be patient.

As with all exercises, accuracy is more important than speed. Everyone is different, so it's important to find the starting tempo that's best for you. Start slowly; speed will come naturally over time.

Divide your time equally between playing with and without the CD. Both have their advantages. Without the CD, your playing is more exposed, so it's easier to notice mistakes or imperfections of accuracy or intonation. With the CD, you can hear how your melodies fit with the chords and rhythm of the recording.

Recording Yourself

Recording your playing can be a very useful tool in evaluating your performance. It gives you the opportunity to hear aspects of your music that might go unnoticed while you're actually playing. Perhaps you're a little flat or sharp. Or maybe you're rushing or dragging the tempo.

Record your improvisations with the CD and then listen to see how it sounds. You might be amazed at how good you sound! The evolution of your music can be greatly accelerated using this method.

> *For purposes of memorization,*
> *listen repeatedly to a recording of the piece you wish to memorize.*

Using a Metronome

Follow the metronome markings for each section. By practicing with a metronome, you will develop accurate rhythm and technique.

Swing Feel

"Swing feel" refers to the rhythm of eighth notes in jazz. While they are written as eighth notes, they're actually played in a triplet feel (Ex. 3).

This means that the downbeat eighth note is longer than the upbeat eighth note.

Furthermore, a slight accent is often placed on the upbeat. This creates a light feeling and a forward motion to the line. Often, students mistakenly accent the downbeat eighth. In order to overcome this, try the following exercises:

1. A. Play even eighths with an exaggerated accent on the upbeat at mm 70 (Ex. 4). Gradually increase to mm 100.

Ex. 4

   B. Then, play Ex. 4 with swing eighths, with a slight accent on the second eighth at mm 70. Gradually increase your tempo to mm 100. Repeat steps A and B daily.

2. In swing feel, at mm 70, read through the music, playing only every second (upbeat) eighth note. Replace the downbeat eighth note with an eighth rest (Ex. 5).

Ex. 5

Swing eighth notes are played in all types of jazz, including Dixieland, swing, bebop, cool, and modal jazz. In Latin styles (such as bossa nova and samba) and rock styles, the eighth notes should be played evenly.

Tips for Memorizing

Memorization of scales, chords, and solos is necessary in order to improvise effectively and creatively. The following are some simple yet effective methods for memorizing:

1. Listen repeatedly to a recording of the piece you wish to memorize until you can sing it with, and then without, the recording. At first, do this slowly so you have time to produce the note your ear is hearing. Try to sing each pitch as closely as possible. Do this every day until you've memorized the melody. If there is no recorded example, record yourself playing and sing with that.

   (All musicians use singing as a means for learning music, even if they're not good singers. After all, the voice is the most basic instrument we have. Your instrument, whether it's a sax, guitar, or piano, is simply an extension of your voice.)

2. Once you can sing the piece, try to play it on your instrument. Once again, do this slowly so you have time to react to what you hear in your head.

3. Play the piece over and over. When you think you know it, look away from the page and try it. Then, read it again, noticing the notes you weren't sure of. Now, look away and try again. Repeat this process every day until you can play it without looking.

Remember: The key to memorization, whether singing, playing, or listening, is repetition.

How to Use This Book

The best way to use this book is to move through Sections One through Four, one key at a time. For example, begin with the D Blues Scale Exercises. When you have completed these, move on to the D Blues Scale One-Bar Ideas. Then, continue with the D Blues Scale Solos Based on the Root, followed by the D Blues Scale Solos Based on the Sixth Degree.

Naturally, some keys are easier than others. I suggest you begin with the blues scales that have only one accidental (an accidental is a flat or sharp). These are D, A, E, and B. The scales with two accidentals, G and F♯, are next; then three accidentals, C, F, and C♯; then four accidentals, B♭ and G♯; and, finally, five accidentals, E♭.

Once you have completed all 12 keys for Sections One through Four, begin Section Five, Blues Scale Solos Based on the Root and the Sixth Degree.

Range Considerations

If a note in this book is too high or low for your instrument's range or your level of study, simply move the note up or down an octave, or replace it with a rest.

Articulation for Wind Players

As a general rule, the music in this book should first be tongued (as smoothly as possible) and then played with the written articulation. The written articulation follows a pattern called up-beat tonguing or "jazz articulation." The pattern is to slur from the up-beat eighth note to the down-beat eighth note. This is the predominant articulation in jazz, Latin, fusion, and blues styles. Therefore, it's an important articulation to master. Once you feel completely comfortable with the jazz articulation, vary it according to what feels natural and sounds good to you. Let yourself be creative.

Listen to recordings and notice how the players articulate. Some players, such as Sonny Stitt and Michael Brecker, are known for their use of jazz articulation. On the other hand, while they often use jazz articulation, Cannonball Adderley and Jerry Bergonzi, for example, are known for their wide variety of tongue/slur combinations.

BLUES SCALE EXERCISES

The following are exercises on each of the 12 blues scales. These exercises will help you develop technical facility with this scale. Apply the following to each key:

1. Begin at mm 60. Play the whole page at one tempo.

2. Once you are able to play a page without any mistakes at approximately mm 84 (with articulation for wind players), begin memorizing it. Memorize one numbered exercise at a time. Eventually, you will be able to play the entire page by memory.

3. Gradually increase your speed to mm 130.

4. Also, try assigning different tempos to each exercise.

Wind players should first legato tongue (Ex. 6) and then slur (Ex. 7) each exercise.

Then, for each Blues Scale Exercise, articulate as marked: up-beat tonguing on numbers 1, 5, and 6; slur two, tongue one on number 2; and slur groups of three on numbers 3 and 4. Notes with reduced noteheads are optional due to range considerations.

D Blues Scale Exercises

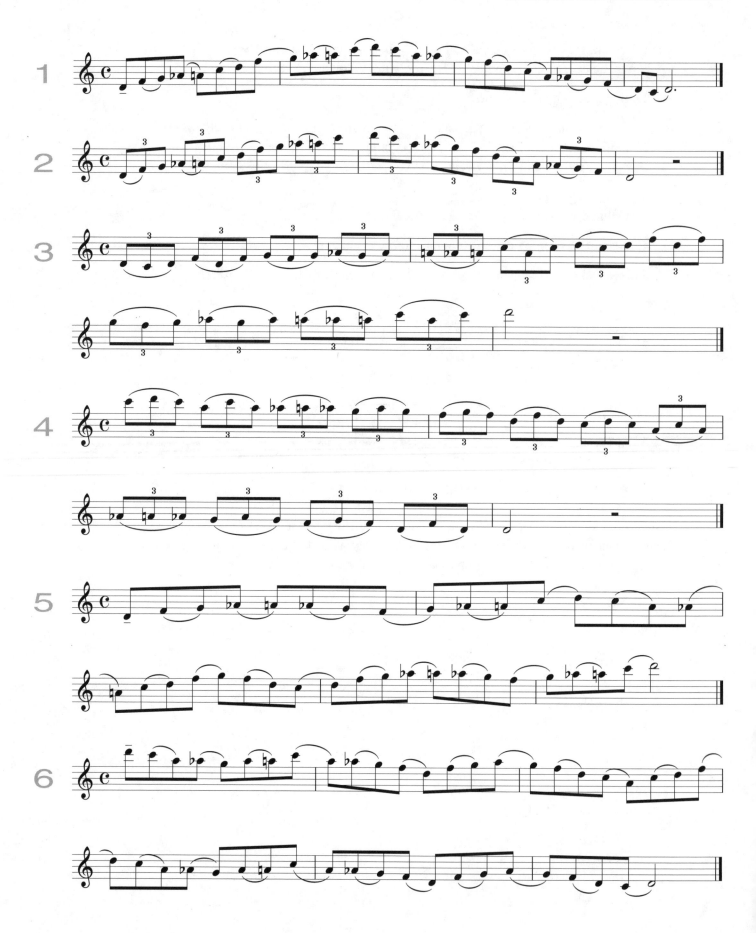

G Blues Scale Exercises

C Blues Scale Exercises

F Blues Scale Exercises

B♭ Blues Scale Exercises

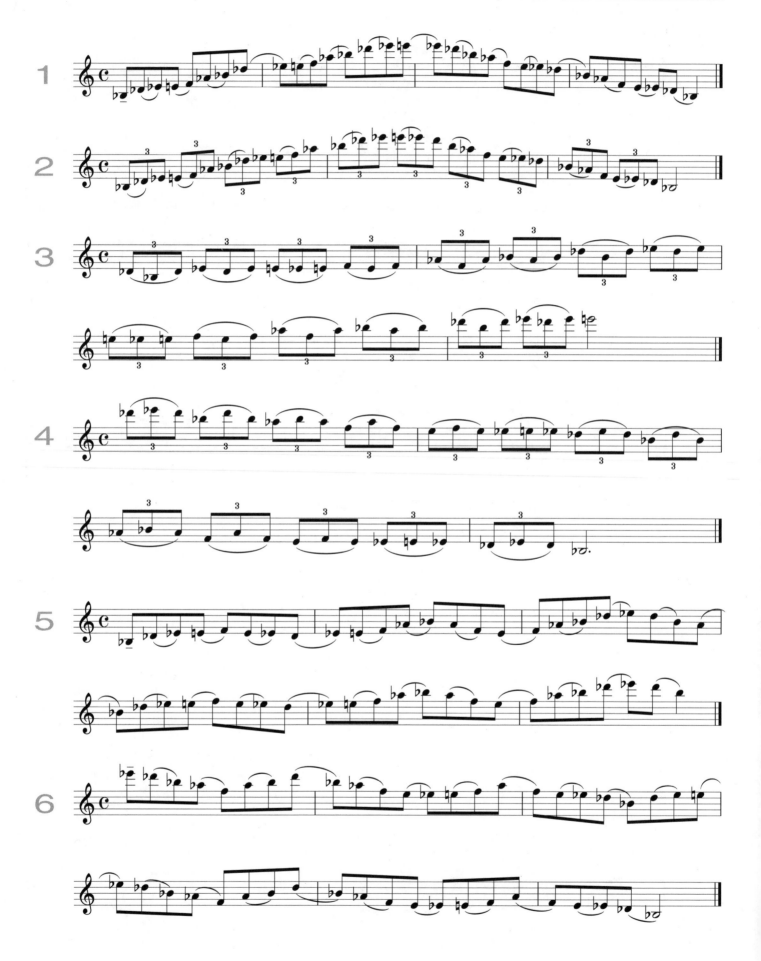

E♭ Blues Scale Exercises

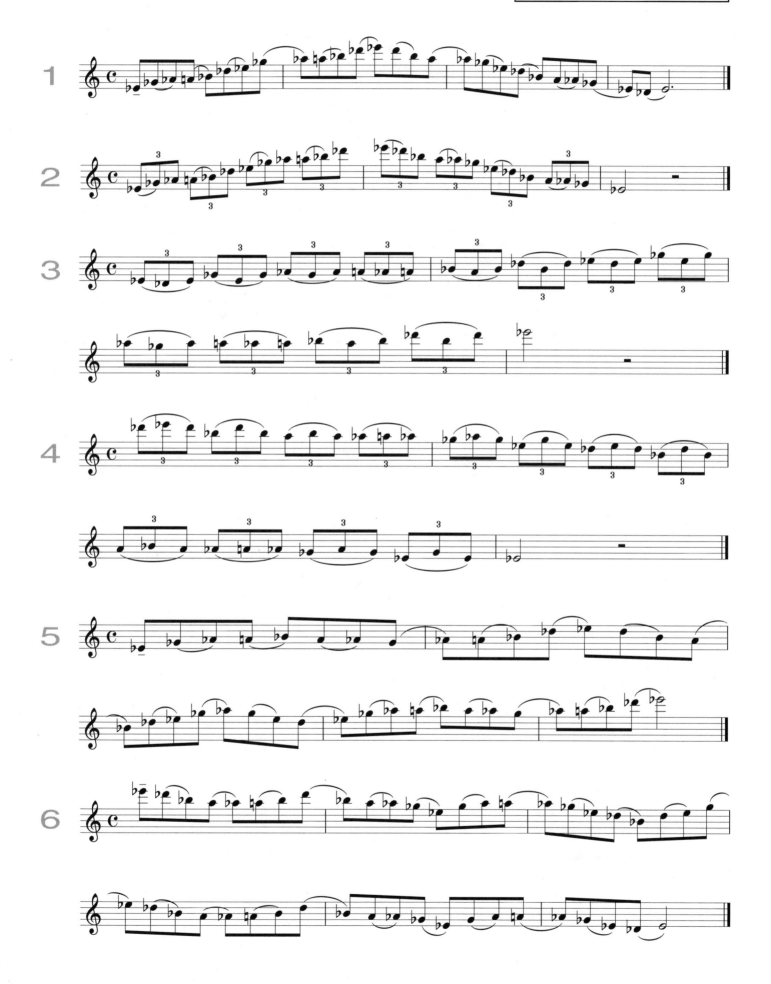

G# Blues Scale Exercises

C# Blues Scale Exercises

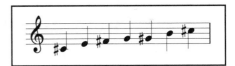

F# Blues Scale Exercises

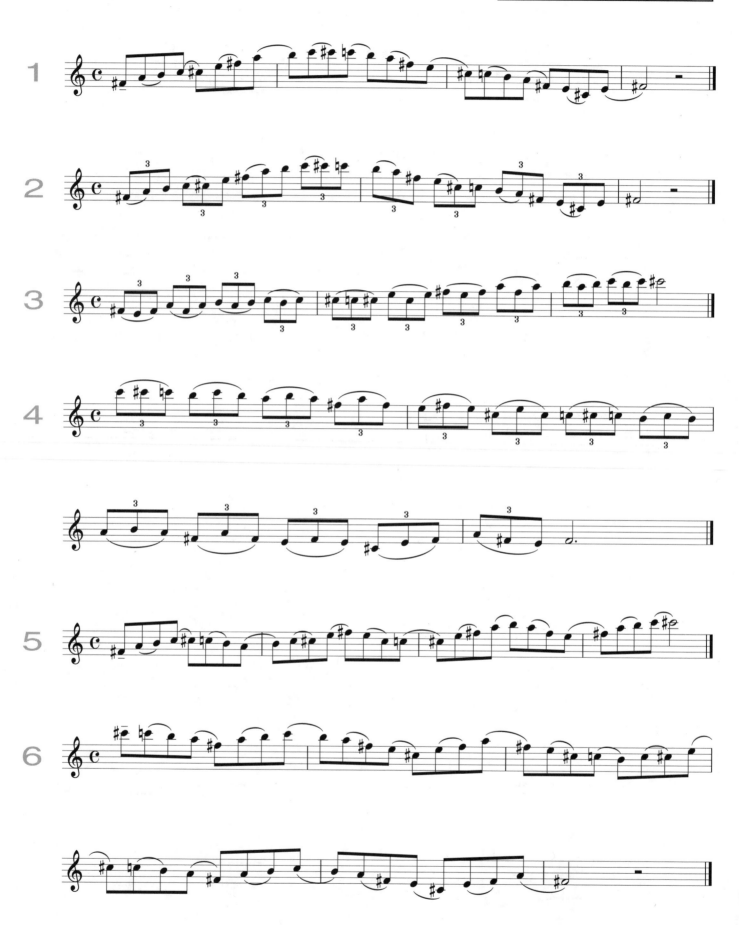

B Blues Scale Exercises

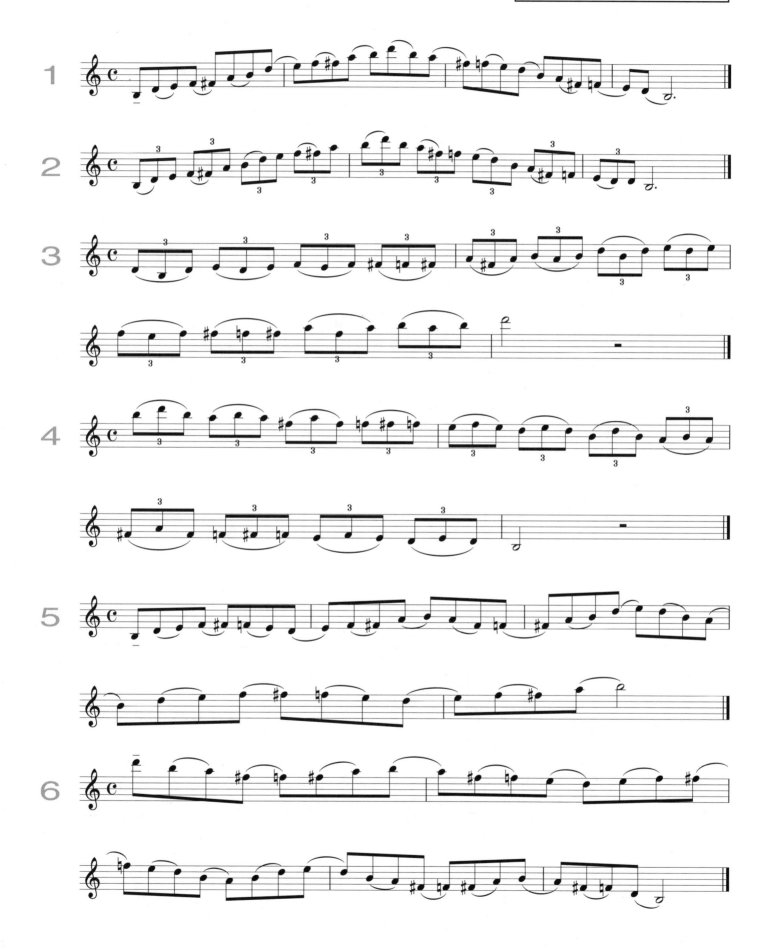

E Blues Scale Exercises

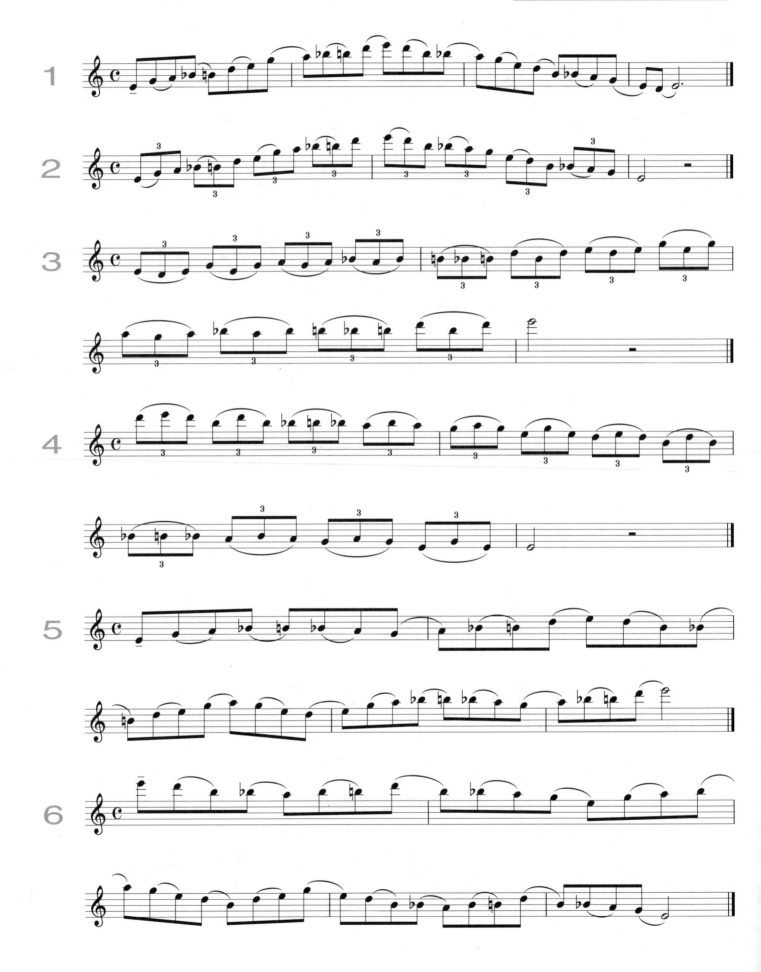

A Blues Scale Exercises

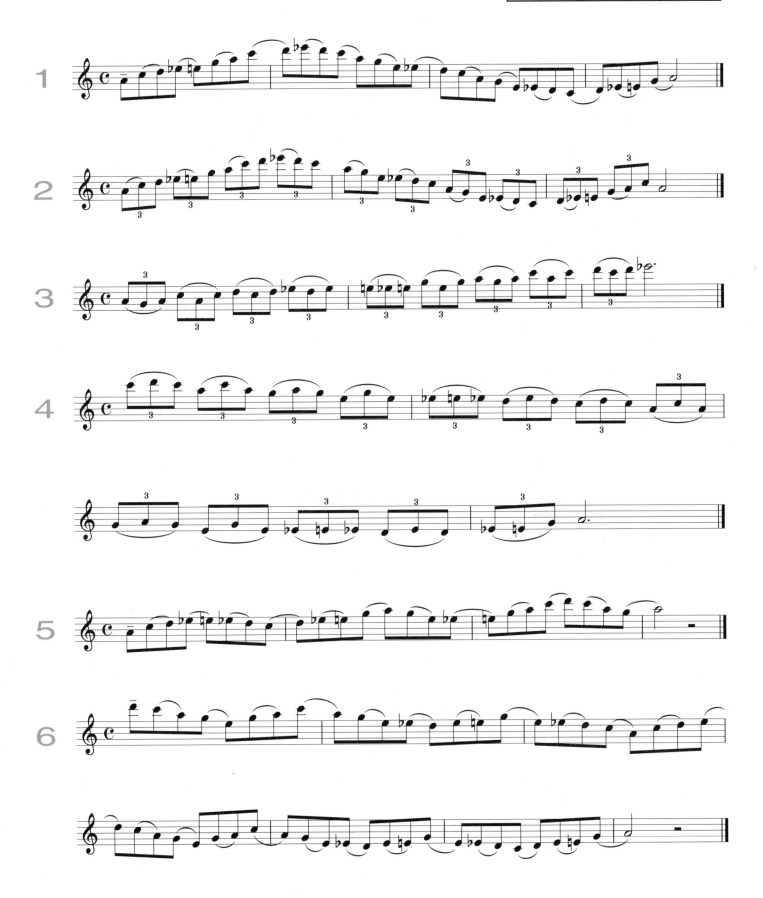

SECTION TWO
BLUES SCALE ONE-BAR IDEAS

These are 24 one-measure melodies using only the blues scale. They are examples of common melodic fragments frequently used by musicians. Notice how they move largely by step, that is, without skipping a note of the scale.

1. Start at mm 80. Wind players: first, tongue every note. Then, articulate as marked.

2. Gradually increase your speed to mm 100.

3. Next play the following exercises with the CD. Make sure to start each one at the beginning of the form:

   a. Play the page as written.

   b. Play each line three times.

   c. Repeat each bar four times.

   d. Repeat each bar two times.

   e. Play each bar followed by one bar of rest.

   f. Play each bar followed by three bars of rest.

   g. Play two bars followed by two bars of rest.

   h. Rest for one bar, play for one bar.

   i. Rest for two bars, play for two bars.

   j. Play the page vertically: bars 1, 5, 9, 13, 17, 21, 2, 6, 10, 14, and so forth.

   k. Skip around the page at random, combining any of the above.

Writing Your Own Ideas, Phrases, and Solos

Writing your ideas down on paper is valuable in the study of improvisation. After all, improvisation is simply composing in the moment. Writing out your solos gives you the opportunity to try different ideas and choose the best ones. It also allows you to see your solos on paper.

This will help you to organize your thinking and decide what works best. It will also, when the time comes, help you to compose in the moment.

Tips for Writing and Improvising With the Blues Scale

Begin using the scale in stepwise motion. This means going up and down the scale without skipping a note. Notice that much of the written material in this book moves by step. Often, we don't need to do much with the scale for it to sound good—it sounds good all by itself!

The scale already has built-in skips (no second or sixth degree). If you skip around too much, it will lose its blues quality. However, some interesting and unusual melodies can result (Ex. 8).

Ex. 8

Rhythms for Improvisation

The following are 24 one-bar rhythms. Notice that they use mostly eighth notes. The eighth note is the predominant rhythm in most jazz, Latin, fusion, blues, and rock.

1. Begin with Rhythm 1. Play it for one chorus using only the root of the D Blues scale (Ex. 9) with the D blues track on the CD.

Ex. 9

2. Then, do this for each of the remaining 23 one-bar rhythms.

3. Next, do the same but use ♭3 (F) of the scale, and then the same on 4 (G) of the scale. Continue this exercise for ♭5 (A♭), 5 (A), and ♭7 (C).

By using the D blues scale over a D blues, we are using the blues scale based on the root of the key. Notice that each degree of the scale has its own characteristic sound. The 1 (D) is the home note. It doesn't need to go anywhere. It sounds resolved.

The 5 (A) is the next most stable note of the scale. It usually sounds fairly resolved and consonant.

The 4 (G) has an ambiguous quality and often sounds as though it wants to move down the scale to the root.

The $\flat 3$ (F), $\flat 5$ (A$\flat$), and $\flat 7$ (C) are referred to as the blue notes. The $\flat 3$ can create a great deal of tension and usually wants to move to the root. It is quite dark and "bluesy." The $\flat 7$, while a little lighter, is also very bluesy and tends to resolve up to the root or down to the 5. The $\flat 5$ is the most dissonant and, therefore, the most dramatic of all the notes. It often resolves down the scale to the root or up to the 5. Its sound is the essence of the blues.

While playing each of these notes, listen to the color and flavor they produce. Then, when you improvise, you will be better able to choose one note over another.

4. Next, play each rhythm using the root and $\flat 3$ (Ex. 10). The order of the notes is up to you. Do this for several choruses each day until you feel confident.

5. Then, play with the root, $\flat 3$, and 4 (Ex. 11). Keep adding notes of the scale until you have all six (or as many as the each rhythm will allow). This is an excellent way to gain rhythmic control and to ease into playing with the entire scale.

6. Tape yourself to see how you sound.

Rhythms for Improvisation

Write Your Own Blues Scale One-Bar Ideas

Try writing your own one-bar ideas:

1. A. Keep the rhythm of bar 1 of the D Blues Scale One-Bar Ideas, but choose different notes from the D blues scale (Ex. 12).

Ex. 12
Rhythm from bar 1; new notes from D blues scale

Move most often by step, either up or down. Practically anything will sound good, so write freely.

   B. Do this for all the bars.

   C. Play and record what you've written with Track 1 of the CD, and listen back to how it sounds. Notice which ones sound best and change the ones you don't like. Then, record it again.

2. A. Take the notes of bar 1 but change the rhythm. Try putting the notes of bar 1 to a rhythm from another bar (Ex. 13), select one from Rhythms for Improvisation on page 26, or simply invent your own. Make sure the rhythm is four beats long.

Ex. 13
Notes from bar 1; rhythm from bar 10

   B. Do this for all the bars.

   C. Play and record it with the CD and listen to how it sounds. Keep the best ones and fix the ones you don't like. Then, record it again.

3. Write your own one-bar ideas. Come up with your own rhythm and notes, and record them with the CD. Rewrite as needed.

Improvising With the Blues Scale One-Bar Ideas

You are ready to improvise with the Blues Scale One-Bar Ideas when you can do the following in any one key:

1. Play the Blues Scale Exercises by memory at mm 100.

2. Play the Blues Scale One-Bar Ideas exercises A–K (as listed on page 24) with the CD.

3. Play your own written one-bar ideas.

Now, continue by improvising your own one-bar ideas using the blues scale for that key. Imitate the sound of the written ideas. Keep it simple and don't think too much. Play what you hear. Try not to be critical of your ideas while you're playing. Enjoy it and have fun!

D Blues Scale One-Bar Ideas

G Blues Scale One-Bar Ideas

C Blues Scale One-Bar Ideas

F Blues Scale One-Bar Ideas

B♭ Blues Scale One-Bar Ideas

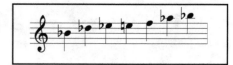

E♭ Blues Scale One-Bar Ideas

G[♯] Blues Scale One-Bar Ideas

C♯ Blues Scale One-Bar Ideas

F♯ Blues Scale One-Bar Ideas

B Blues Scale One-Bar Ideas

E Blues Scale One-Bar Ideas

A Blues Scale One-Bar Ideas

12 24

SECTION THREE
BLUES SCALE SOLOS
BASED ON THE ROOT

The melodic line in these solos uses only the blues scale based on the root of the key. This means that if the blues is in the key of C, then the melody will be comprised of the C blues scale. These solos will serve as models for your own solos. They're designed to be played consecutively, so the last bar in each chorus may contain the pickups to the next chorus.

1. Begin at mm 90 (slower if that's too fast). Wind players should first tongue everything and then play with the written articulation.

2. Gradually increase your speed to mm 120.

3. Try playing with the appropriate CD track.

Tips for Writing and Improvising With the Blues Scale Based on the Root Over a 12-Bar Blues

1. Practice ending phrases on 1 of the key, which is also 1 of the scale. For example, when playing a blues in the key of C, the note C is the 1, or root, of the overall key, and the root of the C blues scale. This note, the root of the key, is the most important note. Notice that many of the written phrases end on the root.

2. Emphasize the roots of the chords. They're included in the blues scale. For example, the chords of a standard blues in C are C7, F7, G7, and sometimes D7 and A7. The roots of these chords are C, F, G, D, and A. The C blues scale contains C, F, and G (Ex. 14).

Ex. 14
C blues scale

While improvising, follow the chord symbols, and begin and/or end your lines with the chord roots. This is a good way of creating a strong solo. Numbers 1, 2, and 8 of the B♭ Blues Scale Solos on B♭ Blues are good examples of this technique. With experience and practice, you will instinctively "hear" these notes.

3. As with the written solos, use primarily eighth notes, eighth-note rests, eighth-note syncopations, occasional triplets, and longer note values such as quarter and half notes and rests.

4. Try writing your own solos, incorporating these ideas.

Phrasing With the Blues Scale

A blues solo is usually comprised of two-bar and four-bar melodic phrases. This fits with the 12-bar form and creates a logical flow of ideas.

Notice the two-bar phrasing throughout the Blues Scale Solos. Numbers 1, 2, and 7 of the F Blues Scale Solos on F Blues are good examples of this. As mentioned, the end of a phrase is usually marked by a longer note or rest (like a half note or a half rest).

Compose your own two-bar phrase and repeat it for one chorus. Now think of another one, and so on.

As previously mentioned, the blues chord progression is divided into three four-bar phrases. Thus, it is logical to create four-bar melodic phrases to complement this. (Incidentally, in this book, each line of music is always four bars long.)

Often, a four-bar melodic phrase is made up of two, two-bar phrases. Look at the F Blues Scale Solos on F Blues Numbers 1, 2, and 5. It's easy to spot the four-bar phrases because the first and second four bars are the same. They are followed by a completely different last four bars. Repeating the first four-bar phrase followed by a new four-bar phrase is a common approach to constructing a blues melody. It is derived from blues lyrics, where the first two lines repeat and the third line is different. Illustrating this are a couple of verses from "Sent for You Yesterday and Here You Come Today" by Jimmy Rushing, Count Basie, and Eddie Durham:

> *Sent for you yesterday and here you come today,*
> *Sent for you yesterday and here you come today,*
> *Baby you can't love me and treat me that-a-way.*
>
> *Ba-by what's on your mind,*
> *Ba-by what's on your mind,*
> *Keep me botherin' and worryin' all the time.*

Improvise or compose your own solos using this four-bar phrase technique. Try combining four Blues Scale One-Bar Ideas for your first and second phrase. Then, combine four new bars for your third phrase.

Improvising With the Blues Scale Based on the Root

You are ready to improvise when you can do the following in any one key:

1. Play the Blues Scale Exercises by memory at mm 100.

2. Play the Blues Scale One-Bar Ideas exercises A–J (on page 24) with the play-along CD (without any mistakes).

3. Play the Blues Scale Solos based on the root with the play-along CD (without mistakes).

4. Hear the downbeat (1) of each measure.

5. Hear the 12-bar form.

6. Hear the beginning of each four-bar phrase.

Next, do the following:

1. Begin by playing the One-Bar Ideas with the play-along CD.

2. Continue by playing the Blues Scale Solos.

3. Improvise using only the blues scale for that key. Imitate the sound of the written solos and ideas. Feel free to go back and forth between the written solos and your own improvisation.

With practice, your improvisation will improve. Keep it simple and stay in control. Have fun! Try to play what you hear in your head.

D Blues Scale Solos on D Blues

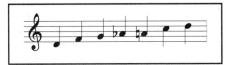

G Blues Scale Solos on G Blues

C Blues Scale Solos on C Blues

F Blues Scale Solos on F Blues

B♭ Blues Scale Solos on B♭ Blues

E♭ Blues Scale Solos on E♭ Blues

54

G♯ Blues Scale Solos on G♯ Blues

C♯ Blues Scale Solos on C♯ Blues*

*Track 20 uses dominant seventh instead of sus4 chords.

F♯ Blues Scale Solos on F♯ Blues

B Blues Scale Solos on B Blues

E Blues Scale Solos on E Blues

A Blues Scale Solos on A Blues

SECTION FOUR
BLUES SCALE SOLOS BASED ON THE SIXTH DEGREE

In addition to using the blues scale based on the root of the key, we can use the blues scale based on the sixth degree of the major scale. In other words, on any blues, we can use two blues scales: one based on the root and the other based on the sixth of the overall key. We can even mix them together. However, for now, we will look at each one separately.

Each scale has its own melodic and harmonic characteristics. The blues scale based on the root is darker, bluesier, and more dramatic. It contains more notes outside the key. The blues scale based on the sixth has a brighter and more major quality.

In addition, each note of the sixth-degree blues scale has a very different character than when the scale is based on the root.

For example, when using the D blues scale on an F blues, the ♭3 (F) is the root of the key, so it is the home note. The ♭7 (C) is the next most stable pitch. The 1 (D) and 4 (G) of the scale are quite consonant but tend to want to resolve to the ♭3 (F). The 5 (A) gives this scale its major quality and can produce a very uplifting sound. Finally, the ♭5 (A♭), once again, is the most dissonant and bluesy note of the scale.

After learning these solos, play each note of the scale for an entire chorus. Listen to the individual characteristics of each note. Then when you improvise, you will be better able to choose one note over another.

Notice how the sound of these solos is lighter and less bluesy than the previous solos. Try to hear the difference by going back and forth between the two.

The solos are designed to be played consecutively, so the last bar in each chorus may contain the pickups to the next chorus.

1. Practice at mm 80. Wind players should first tongue each note and then play with the written articulation.

2. Gradually, increase your tempo to mm 120 or faster.

3. Try writing your own solos.

Tips for Writing or Improvising With the Blues Scale Based on the Sixth Degree

1. Practice beginning and ending phrases on 1 of the key, which is actually ♭3 of the scale. In other words, on a C blues, the note C is the root of the overall key. The blues scale based on the sixth is the A blues scale and C is ♭3 of that scale. This note, the root of the key, is the most important note. D Blues Scale Solos on F Blues Number 2 and E♭ Blues Scale Solos on G♭ Blues Number 2 are good examples of this.

2. Emphasize the roots of the chords. They're included in the blues scale. For example, the chords of a standard blues in C are C7, F7, G7, D–7, and A7. The roots of these chords are C, F, G, D, and A. The A blues scale has C, G, D, and A (Ex. 15). Emphasizing these notes with the corresponding chord is a good way of creating a strong solo.

Ex. 15

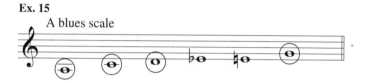

A blues scale

3. As with the written solos, use primarily eighth notes, eighth-note rests, eighth-note syncopations, triplets, and longer note values such as quarter and half notes and rests.

4. Try writing your own solos incorporating these ideas.

Developing an Idea

An additional technique for writing or improvising is to begin with a melodic or rhythmic idea and change it slightly. For instance, write a one-, two-, or four-bar melody and repeat it, changing some of the notes but keeping the rhythm the same (Ex. 16).

Ex. 16

original melody   melodic variation

Or change the rhythm slightly but keep the notes (Ex. 17).

Ex. 17

original melody   rhythmic variation

You can even change both the notes and rhythm, as long as the result still sounds close to the original (Ex. 18).

Ex. 18

original melody   melodic and rhythmic variation

One approach is to simply play the same melody starting from one note higher in the scale. E♭ and C Blues Scale Solos on E♭ Blues, Number 4 is a good example of this. Try applying this to a written chorus.

By developing an original idea in this way, you can create infinite melodic and rhythmic variations. You can structure an entire chorus or two around one idea. This technique creates a logical and musical flow. It's as though you're telling a story with melody.

Known as thematic development or variations on a theme, this device is commonly used by jazz, blues, and rock musicians to create interesting solos. In classical music, its use dates back to the early 1500s. Composers such as Bach, Mozart, and Beethoven wrote fugues and entire movements of symphonies around a single theme.

The following are some examples of this technique: F Blues Scale Solos on F Blues, Number 7; D Blues Scale Solos on D Blues, Number 7; B Blues Scale Solos on D Blues, Numbers 1 and 3; G and E Blues Scale Solos on G Blues, Number 1.

Improvising With the Blues Scale Based on the Sixth Degree

You are ready to improvise when you can do the following in any one key:

1. Play the Blues Scale Exercises by memory at mm 100.

2. Play the Blues Scale Solos (based on the sixth degree) with the CD.

3. Hear the downbeat (1) of each measure.

4. Hear the 12-bar form.

5. Hear the beginning of each four-bar phrase.

For improvisation, follow these steps with the CD:

1. Begin by playing the Blues Scale Solos (based on the sixth degree).

2. Play your written solos.

3. Improvise using the blues scale based on the sixth degree, imitating the sound of the written solos. Follow the suggestions for improvising with the blues scale.

B Blues Scale Solos on D Blues

E Blues Scale Solos on G Blues

A Blues Scale Solos on C Blues

D Blues Scale Solos on F Blues

G Blues Scale Solos on B♭ Blues

74

C Blues Scale Solos on E♭ Blues

F Blues Scale Solos on A♭ Blues

B♭ Blues Scale Solos on D♭ Blues

*Track 20 uses dominant seventh instead of sus4 chords.

E♭ Blues Scale Solos on G♭ Blues

G# Blues Scale Solos on B Blues

C# Blues Scale Solos on E Blues

11 23

F♯ Blues Scale Solos on A Blues

BLUES SCALE SOLOS BASED ON THE ROOT AND THE SIXTH DEGREE

Since we can use two different blues scales (one based on the root, the other on the sixth) on any 12-bar blues, why not use them both together, alternating back and forth between the two? In fact, this is common practice among professional musicians. It gives you the opportunity to choose, at any given moment, whether to use the bright, major-sounding sixth degree scale or the dark, bluesier, root-based scale.

The following are model solos that use both of these scales. They are designed to be played consecutively, so the last bar in each chorus may contain the pickups to the next chorus.

1. Begin around mm 90. Wind players should first tongue everything and then play with the written articulation.

2. Gradually increase your speed to mm 120.

3. Try writing your own solos. Follow the tips for writing with these scales.

Tips for Writing and Improvising Using the Blues Scales Based on the Root and Sixth Degree

The main thing to remember when writing or improvising with both scales is to keep them separate and intact. We want the characteristics of each scale to come through. If we blend them together, the resulting scale won't sound like either. In fact, it won't even sound like a blues scale.

As you gain experience, depending on which sound you wish to hear, you will instinctively choose one scale over another. However, in the meantime, practice the following exercises:

1. Alternate choruses. First chorus: improvise with the blues scale based on the sixth. Second chorus: improvise with the blues scale based on the root, and so on.

2. Now alternate every four bars. First four bars: sixth scale. Second four bars: root scale. Third four bars: back to sixth scale. Then reverse the order.

3. Try switching scales every two bars.

4. For a practically endless variety of solos, try combining the Blues Scale Solos Based on the Root with the Blues Scale Solos Based on the Sixth Degree. For example, take the C Blues Scale Solos on C Blues and the A Blues Scale Solos on C Blues and try alternating lines from each. You could play the first line of the A Blues Scale Solo Number 1, followed by the second line of the C Blues Scale Solo Number 1, and so on. Some combinations will sound better than others, so experiment until you find the best ones. Remember: When improvising or writing, don't skip around too much! For further suggestions, refer back to Tips for Writing and Improvising with the Blues Scale Over a 12-Bar Blues on page 41.

Improvising With Both the Blues Scale Based on the Root and the Sixth Degree

You are ready to improvise when you can do the following on the blues scales based on the root and sixth of any one key:

1. Play the Blues Scale Exercises by memory at mm 100.

2. Play the Blues Scale Solos Based on the Root and the Sixth Degree with the CD (without any mistakes).

3. Hear the downbeat (1) of each measure.

4. Hear the 12-bar form.

5. Hear the beginning of each four-bar phrase.

For improvisation, follow these steps with the CD:

1. Begin by playing the solos.

2. Improvise using the two blues scales. Imitate the sound of the written solos. Follow the tips for improvising with these two scales.

D and B Blues Scale Solos
on D Blues

84

G and E Blues Scale Solos
on G Blues

C and A Blues Scale Solos
on C Blues

F and D Blues Scale Solos
on F Blues

Bb and G Blues Scale Solos on Bb Blues

Eb and C Blues Scale Solos on Eb Blues

A♭ and F Blues Scale Solos on A♭ Blues

For ease of reading, the C♭ note has been written as B♮ in these exercises.

C♯ and B♭ Blues Scale Solos on C♯ Blues

* For ease of reading, the B♭ blues scale has been written as an A♯ blues scale.
Track 20 uses dominant seventh chords instead of sus4 chords.

F♯ and E♭ Blues Scale Solos
on F♯ Blues

For ease of reading, the E♭ blues scale has been written as a D♯ blues scale.

B and G# Blues Scale Solos on B Blues

E and C# Blues Scale Solos on E Blues

A and F# Blues Scale Solos on A Blues

50 BLUES LICKS

Blues Licks

The following are some common blues scale licks that fit over a D blues. They are mostly made up of the D blues scale; a few borrow notes from the B blues scale. First, play them over the appropriate CD track. Then, choose two and transpose them into 12 keys. Memorize them and put them into your improvised solos. Then, memorize some more. As you increase your repertoire of licks, you can combine them for infinite variations.

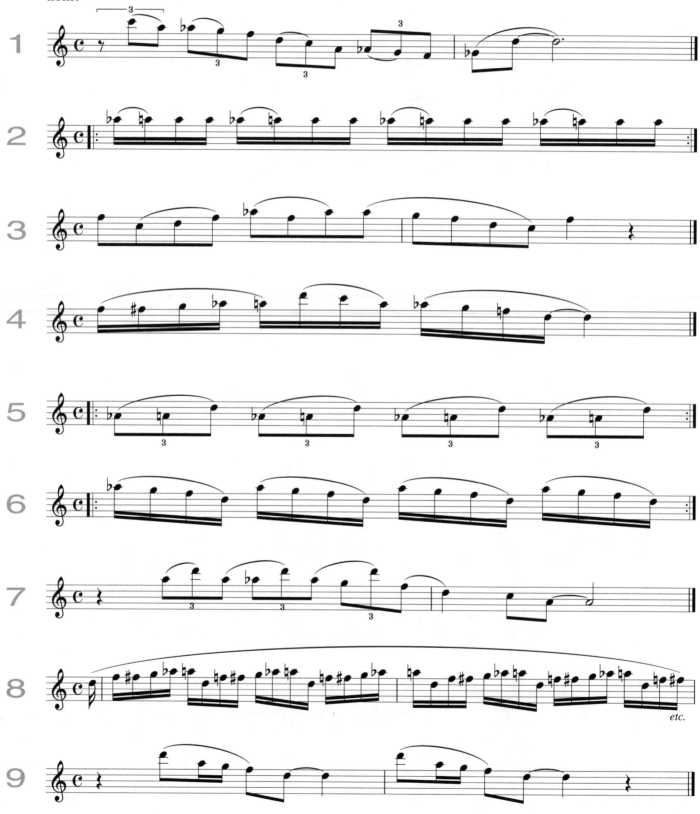

etc.

98

FUNK ONE-BAR RHYTHMS AND SOLOS

Funk One-Bar Rhythms

Several of the tracks on the CD are in a funk style. The following are 48 funk one-bar rhythmic ideas. Notice the large number of sixteenth notes. Sixteenth-note syncopations and rests are common in funk.

1. Play, as written, at mm 60 and gradually increase your tempo to mm 106.

2. Then, begin with bar 1. Repeat it for one chorus with Track 4, using only the root of the scale, based on the root.

3. Do this for each of the remaining 47 one-bar rhythms. As you repeat each bar individually, ignore any ties that connect one bar to the next.

4. Try these rhythms with other notes from the two blues scales.

5. Write your own blues scale melodies using these rhythms.

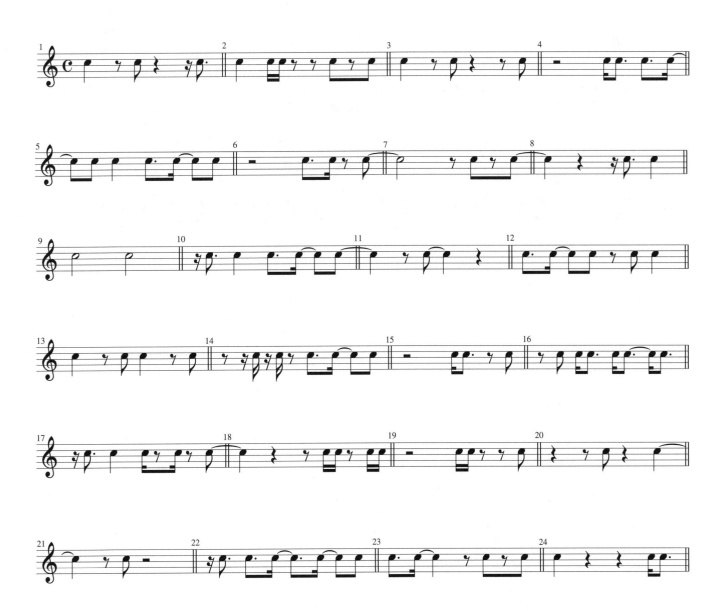

Blues Scale Funk Solos

The following solos feature common funk rhythms drawn from the 48 Funk One-Bar Rhythms. They are comprised of both the blues scale based on the root and the sixth degree. Practice them slowly. Once you have learned them, try playing with the CD. Then, try writing and improvising your own solos.

Uh Uh!

Ahhh...

*For ease of reading, the B♭ blues scale has been written as an A♯ blues scale.

Huh?

O u c h !

1

2

TRADITIONAL BLUES SONGS

County Farm Blues

Analysis: Combination of F♯ and A blues scales

Son House

1. Down South—— when you do an-y-thing that's wrong,——

Down—— South when you do an-y-thing that's

wrong. Down—— South,———— when you

do an-y-thing———— that's wrong, they'll sure—— put you

down on the Coun-ty Farm——

Come Back Baby

Analysis: B blues scale plus C♯ from G♯ blues scale

Snooks Eaglin

1. Come back, ba - by,_____ Please___ don't go,_____ For the way I love you, ba -

by, You'll nev - er know._____ Come back, ba - by, Let's talk it o -

ver, One more time._____

Worrying You Off My Mind

Analysis: Combination of E♭ and F♯ blues scale

Big Bill Broonzy

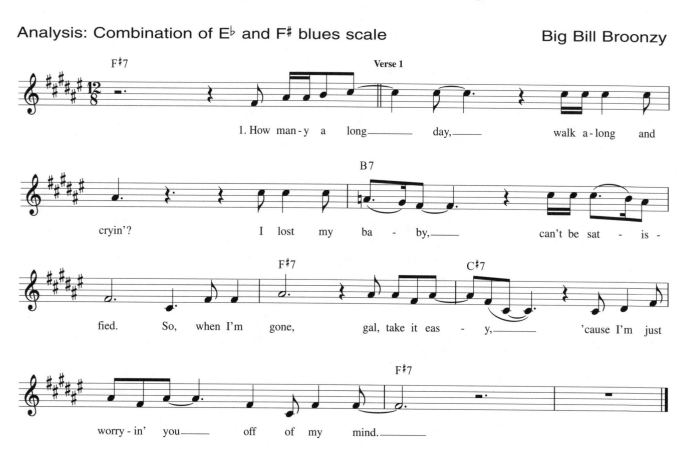

1. How man - y a long_____ day,_____ walk a - long and

cryin'? I lost my ba - by,_____ can't be sat - is -

fied. So, when I'm gone, gal, take it eas - y,_____ 'cause I'm just

worry - in' you_____ off of my mind._____

Drunken Barrel House Blues

Analysis: Combination of F♯ and A blues scales

Memphis Minnie

1. If— you— lis-ten to me good,— peo - ple,—

I'll tell you what it's all a - bout,—

If— you lis - ten to me good,— peo - ple,—

I'll tell you what it's all a - bout.—

Well, the good stuff is— here,—

And it's just for— now.—

Green River Blues

Analysis: F♯ blues scale plus B♭ from E♭ blues scale

Charlie Patton

1. I (went up Green Riv - er) roll - in' like a log,

I wade up Green River

roll - in' like a log,

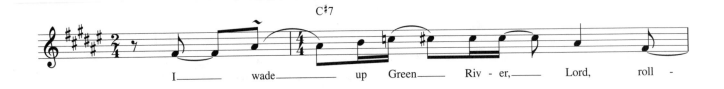

I wade up Green River, Lord, roll -

- in' like a log.

110

Meat Shakin' Woman

Analysis: Combination of D and B blues scales

Recorded by
Blind Boy Fuller

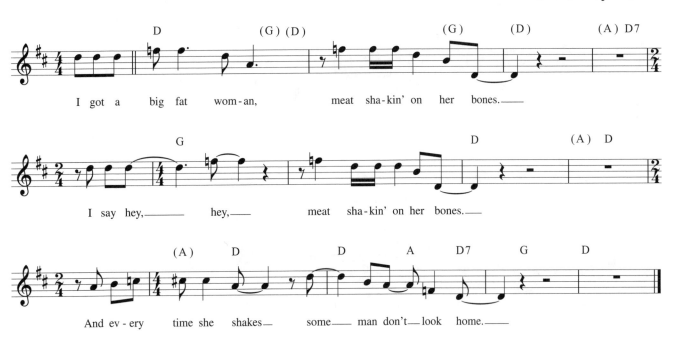

I got a big fat wom-an, meat sha-kin' on her bones.

I say hey, hey, meat sha-kin' on her bones.

And ev - ery time she shakes some man don't look home.

Mistreated Blues

Analysis: F♯ blues scale plus A♯ from D♯ blues scale

Recorded by
Henry Townsend

1. My ba-by just mis-treats me night and day.

If my sweet wom-an just mis - treat me

night and day, and she

mis-treats this poor man just to pass the dog-gone time a - way.

Police Dog Blues

Analysis: E blues scale plus G# from C# blues scale

Blind Blake

1. All my life___ I been a trav'-lin' man.___

All my life___ I've been a trav'-lin' man.___

Stay-in' a-lone___ and do-in'___ the best___ I can.

Shuckin' Sugar

Analysis: Combination of A and F# blues scales

Recorded by
Blind Lemon Jefferson

I've got your pic-ture,___ and I'm go-ing to put it in___ a frame.___ I've got

your pic-ture, I put it in___ a frame,___ shuck-in' sug-ar,___ And then if you___

___ leave town___ we can___ spot___ you just___ the same.___

BLUES SCALES

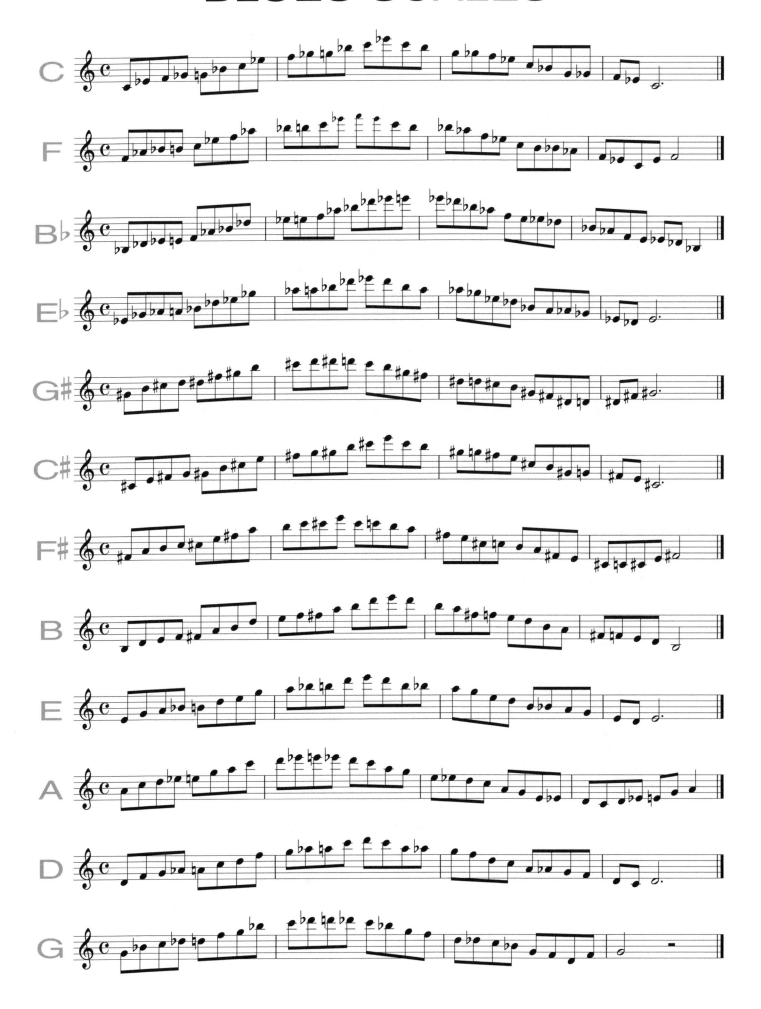

45 RECORDED EXCERPTS FOR LISTENING AND TRANSCRIBING

Listening to a wide variety of music, both recorded and live, is one of the most important and effective ways of learning to play well. For the purposes of this book, we are particularly interested in listening to recordings of 12-bar blues and blues scale usage.

By listening to master musicians, as well as to our favorite players, we learn a great deal without even trying. Often, much of what we've heard emerges in our playing automatically. After a great deal of listening, nuances of inflection and tone, as well as actual melodies, begin to appear as if by magic.

In addition, we can take a more deliberate approach to learning from recordings. Have you ever heard a song in the morning and then couldn't get it out of your head all day? Imagine if that song were an unbelievable blues lick by B.B. King. You listened to it every day for a week so that it never stopped ringing in your head. Then, you started singing or whistling it. Then, you figured it out on your instrument and successfully learned it in several keys. Next, you began the process all over with a new lick. This is called transcribing. When we transcribe, we are learning directly from the source. All improvising musicians eventually transcribe their favorite recorded solos and licks. This enables us to study, understand, and incorporate the styles of the great players who came before us. It all begins with listening—the more the better.

The following recorded excerpts are made up almost entirely of blues scales. By listening to these recordings and transcribing these solos, you will learn a great deal about how master musicians improvise and compose with blues scales.

Each blues scale analysis is transposed for B♭ instruments.

Louis Armstrong
The Smithsonian Collection of Classic Jazz
> "Struttin' with Some Barbeque" (Lillian Hardin Armstrong)
> Chorus 1, bars 1–6 of trumpet solo
> Analysis: G blues scale

Sidney Bechet
The Complete Blue Note Recordings of Sidney Bechet, Blue Note
> "Blue Horizon" (Sidney Bechet)
> Analysis: Entire clarinet solo is a blend of D and F blues scales

Bob Berg
Short Stories, Denon
> "Friday Night at the Cadillac Club" (Bob Berg)
> Bars 23–31 of tenor saxophone solo
> Analysis: D blues scale

Michael Brecker
A Prescription for the Blues, Horace Silver; Impulse!
> "Yodel Lady Blues" (Horace Silver)
> First 16 bars of tenor saxophone solo
> Analysis: F blues scale

Larry Carlton
Larry Carlton, Warner
"Room 335" (Larry Carlton)
Bars 32–41 of guitar solo vamp
Analysis: G# blues scale

Eric Clapton
Disraeli Gears, Cream; Atco
"Tales of Brave Ulysses" (Eric Clapton and Martin Sharp)
4-bar guitar solo at the end of second verse
Analysis: B blues scale

"The Sunshine of Your Love" (Jack Bruce, Pete Brown, and Eric Clapton)
Guitar solo (28 measures)
Analysis: combines E and C# blues scales

"Outside Woman Blues" (Arthur Reynold)
Guitar solo (12 bars)
Analysis: F# blues scale

Paul Desmond
Time Out, Dave Brubeck; Columbia
"Blue Rondo a la Turk" (Dave Brubeck)
Chorus 1, bars 1–3 (G blues scale) and chorus 2, bars 1–5 (blend of G and E blues scale) of alto saxophone solo

Eric Dolphy
Outward Bound, Prestige
"245" (Eric Dolphy)
Chorus 2, bars 1–6 of alto saxophone solo
Analysis: G blues scale (with E borrowed from E blues scale)

Antonio Hart
Here I Stand, Impulse!
"Like My Own" (Antonio Hart)
Melody (14 bars)
Analysis: F# and A blues scales

Joe Henderson
Song for My Father, Horace Silver; Blue Note
"Song for My Father" (Horace Silver)
Chorus 2, bars 9–16 of tenor saxophone solo
Analysis: G blues scale

Jimi Hendrix
Axis: Bold as Love, Reprise
"Up From the Skies" (Jimi Hendrix)
Bars 1–15 of guitar solo
Analysis: G# blues scale

Jimi Hendrix
Are You Experienced?, Reprise
"Manic Depression" (Jimi Hendrix)
Bars 1–16 of guitar solo
Analysis: B blues scale

B.B. King
My Sweet Little Angel, Flair
"Why Did You Leave Me" (B.B. King and Jules Bihari)
Guitar solo (12 bars)
Analysis: C blues scale

B.B. King
Do the Boogie! B.B. King's Early '50s Classics, Flair
"Everything I Do Is Wrong" (B.B. King and Joe Bihari)
Guitar solo (12 bars)
Analysis: A blues scale

B.B. King
The RPM Hits From 1951–1957, Ace
"Please Hurry Home" (B.B. King and Jules Bihari)
Guitar solo (12 bars)
Analysis: A blues scale (with C# borrowed from F# blues scale)

B.B. King
Singin' the Blues/The Blues, Flair
"Three O'Clock Blues" (B.B. King and Jules Bihari)
Guitar solo (12 bars)
Analysis: C and A blues scales

"You Upset Me Baby" (B.B. King and Jules Bihari)
Guitar solo (8 bars)
Analysis: a blend of F# and A blues scales

Herbie Mann
At the Village Gate, Atlantic
"Comin' Home Baby" (Herbie Mann)
Analysis: Entire flute solo around A blues scale

Pat Martino
El Hombre, Prestige
"Cisco" (Pat Martino)
Chorus 5, bars 1–6 of guitar solo
Analysis: A blues scale

Jack McDuff
The Honeydripper, Prestige
"The Honeydripper" (Joe Liggins)
Chorus 4, bars 1–12 of organ solo
Analysis: C blues scale

Lee Morgan
Blue Train, John Coltrane; Blue Note
"Blue Train" (John Coltrane)
Chorus 5, bars 1–7 of trumpet solo
Analysis: F blues scale

Charlie Parker
Now's the Time, Verve
"Now's the Time" (Charlie Parker)
Chorus 2, bars 4–6 of alto saxophone solo
Analysis: G blues scale

Maceo Parker
Southern Exposure, Novus
> "Keep Marching On" (Neville/Porter/Nocentelli/Modeliste)
> Bars 8–16 of alto saxophone solo vamp
> Analysis: D blues scale

> "Blues for Shorty Bill" (Maceo Parker)
> Melody and alto saxophone solo
> Analysis: A blues scale with F♯ borrowed from F♯ blues scale

Oscar Peterson
Very Tall, Verve
> "Reunion Blues" (Milt Jackson)
> Chorus 1–3 (36 bars) of piano solo
> Analysis: blend of G and E blues scales

Oscar Peterson
Affinity, Verve
> "Gravy Waltz" (Oscar Peterson)
> Melody and chorus 1 (32 bars) of piano solo
> Analysis: mix of A and F♯ blues scales

David Sanborn
Straight to the Heart, Warner
> "Straight to the Heart" (Marcus Miller)
> Bars 4–11 of alto saxophone solo
> Analysis: D blues scale; entire 48-bar solo made up almost entirely of D and F blues scales

David Sanborn
Double Vision, Warner
> "Maputo" (Marcus Miller)
> Bars 11–21 of coda alto saxophone solo
> Analysis: A blues scale (without E)

David Sanborn
As We Speak, Warner
> "Rain on Christmas" (David Sanborn)
> Bar 10–13 of alto saxophone solo
> Analysis: B and D blues scales

Larry Schneider
We Will Meet Again, Bill Evans; Warner
> "Five" (Bill Evans)
> Bars 25–35 of tenor saxophone solo
> Analysis: C blues scale

Jimmy Smith
Back at the Chicken Shack (Jimmy Smith)
> Chorus 3 (12 bars) of organ solo
> Analysis: mix of G and E blues scales; entire solo is built around these two scales

Mike Stern
Back Roads, Bob Berg; Denon
       "Silverado" (Bob Berg)
       Bars 1–9 of guitar solo
       Analysis: D blues scale

Mike Stern
Jigsaw, Atlantic
       Chorus 3, bars 1–4 of guitar solo
       Analysis: D blues scale

Stanley Turrentine
Sugar, CTI
       "Sugar" (Stanley Turrentine)
       Chorus 5, bars 8–16 of tenor saxophone solo
       Analysis: D blues scale

Stanley Turrentine
A Chip Off the Old Block, Blue Note
       "Cherry Point"
       Chorus 3, bars 1–8 of tenor saxophone solo
       Analysis: C and A blues scales

Van Halen
For Unlawful Carnal Knowledge, Warner
       "Pleasure Dome" (Edward Van Halen, Alex Van Halen, Michael Anthony, and
          Sammy Hagar)
       Bars 1–8 of guitar solo
       Analysis: E$\flat$ blues scale

       "In 'n' Out" (Edward Van Halen, Alex Van Halen, Michael Anthony, and
          Sammy Hagar)
       Guitar solo (24 bars)
       Analysis: G$\sharp$ and B blues scales

       "Man on a Mission" (Edward Van Halen, Alex Van Halen, Michael Anthony, and
          Sammy Hagar)
       Guitar solo (8 bars)
       Analysis: F$\sharp$ blues scale

       "Runaround" (Edward Van Halen, Alex Van Halen, Michael Anthony, and
          Sammy Hagar)
       Guitar solo (16 bars)
       Analysis: B blues scale

       "Right Now" (Edward Van Halen, Alex Van Halen, Michael Anthony, and Sammy
          Hagar)
       Guitar solo (8 bars)
       Analysis: E blues scale

Van Halen
1984, Warner
> "Jump" (Edward Van Halen, Alex Van Halen, Michael Anthony, and
>> David Lee Roth)
> Guitar solo (8 bars)
> Analysis: C blues scale

Kirk Whalum
Caché, Columbia
> "Living in the Streets" (K. Whalum, R. Lawson)
> Melody and tenor saxophone solo
> Analysis: F# blues scale with modulation to A blues scale for 8 bars during solo

Lester Young
The Sound of Jazz
> "Fine and Mellow" (Billie Holiday)
> Tenor saxophone solo (12 bars)
> Analysis: D blues scale

15 TUNES THAT ARE PREDOMINANTLY COMPOSED OF THE BLUES SCALE

1. "Birks Works" (Dizzy Gillespie). All in G blues scale.

2. "Centerpiece" (Harry Eddison and Bill Tennyson). All in G blues scale.

3. "Everyday I Have the Blues" (Peter Chatman). Performed by B.B. King. All in C and A blues scales.

4. "Goodbye Porkpie Hat" (Charles Mingus). All in G blues scale, except for four notes.

5. "Jig-a-Jug" (Joshua Redman). All in C and E♭ blues scales.

6. "Like My Own" (Antonio Hart). All in B and D blues scale.

7. "Moanin'" (Bobby Timmons). All in G blues scale.

8. "Outside Woman Blues" (Arthur Reynold). Performed by Cream. All in F♯ blues scale, except for one note from E♭ blues scale.

9. "Pfrancing" (Miles Davis). All in G blues scale.

10. "Purple Haze" (Jimi Hendrix). All in E♭ and F♯ blues scales.

11. "Sponge" (Randy Brecker). Performed by the Brecker Brothers. All in G blues scale.

12. "Three O'Clock Blues" (B.B. King). All in C blues scale.

13. "Tuxedo Junction" (Erskine Hawkins, William Johnson, and Julian Dash). All in A blues scale, except for one note.

14. "Watermelon Man" (Herbie Hancock). All in E blues scale with one note from G blues scale.

15. "The Wind Cries Mary" (Jimi Hendrix). All in E blues scale.

RECOMMENDED LISTENING

Cannonball Adderley *Mercy, Mercy, Mercy* / 1966 / Capitol

Albert Ammons *The First Day* / 1939 / Blue Note

Louis Armstrong *Hot Five and Hot Sevens,* Vol. 3 / 1927–8 / Columbia

Art Blakey and the Jazz Messengers *The Freedom Rider* / 1961 / Blue Note

Brecker Brothers *Straphanin'* / 1980 / One Way

Michael Brecker *Tales from the Hudson* / 1996 / Impulse

Dave Brubeck *Time Out* / 1959 / Columbia

Ray Charles *Best of Atlantic* / 1994 / Rhino

Eric Clapton *The Cream of Clapton* / 1995 / Polydor

Albert Collins *Ice Pickin'* / 1978 / Alligator

John Coltrane *Coltrane Plays the Blues* / 1960 / Atlantic

Chick Corea *Now He Sings, Now He Sobs* / 1968 / Blue Note

James Cotton *100% Cotton* / 1974 / One Way

Hank Crawford *On the Blue Side* / 1989 / Milestone

King Curtis *Instant Soul: The Legendary King Curtis* / 1994

Miles Davis *Kind of Blue* / 1959 / Columbia

Duke Ellington *The Carnegie Hall Concerts (January 1943)* / Prestige

Kenny G *Duotones* / 1986 / Arista

Kenny Garrett *Pursuance: The Music of John Coltrane* / 1996 / Warner Bros.

Dizzy Gillespie *Duets with Sonny Rollins and Sonny Stitt* / 1957 / Verve

Buddy Guy *The Very Best of Buddy Guy* / 1992 / Rhino

Herbie Hancock *Headhunters* / 1973 / Columbia

Gene Harris *Introducing the Three Sounds* / 1958 / Blue Note

Jimi Hendrix *Axis: Bold As Love* / 1967 / Reprise

John Lee Hooker *John Lee Hooker Plays and Sings the Blues* / 1961 / MCA/Chess

Lightin' Hopkins *Mojo Hand: The Anthology* / 1993 / Rhino

Son House *Son House & the Great Delta Blues Singers* / 1990 / Document

Mississippi John Hurt *1928 Sessions* / 1988 / Yazoo

B.B. King *Singin' the Blues/The Blues* / 1992 / Flair

Herbie Mann *At the Village Gate* / 1961 / Atlantic

Wynton Marsalis *Standard Time,* Vol. 1 / 1986 / Columbia

Pat Martino *Live!* / 1972 / Muse

Wes Montgomery *The Incredible Jazz Guitar of Wes Montgomery* / 1960 /
    Original Jazz Classics

Oliver Nelson *Blues and the Abstract Truth* / 1961 / Impulse!

Charlie Parker *Now's the Time* / 1952 / Verve

Joshua Redman *Spirit of the Moment: Live at the Village Vanguard* / 1995 /
    Warner Bros.

Sonny Rollins *Saxophone Colossus* / 1956 / Prestige

Otis Rush *Cobra Recordings 1956–1958* / 1989 / Paula/Flyright

David Sanborn *Straight to the Heart* / 1984 / Warner Brothers

John Scofield *Hand Jive* / 1993 / Blue Note

Tom Scott *Bluestreak* / 1996 / GRP

Horace Silver *Song for My Father* / 1964 / Blue Note

Bessie Smith *The Bessie Smith Collection (Columbia Jazz Masterpieces)* / 1989 /
    Columbia

Jimmy Smith *Back at the Chicken Shack* / 1960 / Blue Note

Roosevelt Sykes *Boogie Honky Tonk* / Oldie Blues

Big Joe Turner *Jumpin' the Blues* / 1948 / Arho

Stanley Turrentine *Let It Go* / 1966 / GRP / Impulse

Stevie Ray Vaughan *Greatest Hits* / 1995 / Epic

Grover Washington, Jr. *Winelight* / 1980 / Elektra

Muddy Waters *The Best of Muddy Waters* / 1987 / MCA/Chess

Howlin' Wolf *Howlin' Wolf Rides Again* / 1993 / Flair-Virgin

Lester Young *Count Basie and His Orchestra 1936–1938* / 1990 / Classics

Music Business and Reference Books from Berklee Press

COMPLETE GUIDE TO FILM SCORING ▸ by Richard Davis
Learn the art and business of writing music for films and TV. Topics include: the film-making process, preparing and recording a score, contracts and fees, publishing, royalties, and copyrights. Features interviews with 19 film-scoring professionals.
50449417 Book...$24.95

THE CONTEMPORARY SINGER ▸ by Anne Peckham
Maximize your vocal potential by learning how to use and protect your voice properly. Develop stage presence, microphone technique, stamina, range, and sound with exercises for all voice ranges and types on the accompanying CD. Includes lead sheets for such standard vocal repertoire pieces as *Yesterday, I'm Beginning to See the Light,* and *I Heard It Through the Grapevine.*
50449438 Book/CD $24.95

ESSENTIAL EAR TRAINING ▸ by Steve Prosser
Step-by-step introduction to the basics of ear training and sight singing, as taught at Berklee College of Music. Develop your inner ear and musical vocabulary, learn to hear the music you see, understand the music you hear, and notate the music you have composed or arranged. Complete course with rhythmic and melodic studies using conducting patterns.
50449421 Book...$14.95

HOW TO GET A JOB IN THE MUSIC AND RECORDING INDUSTRY ▸ by Keith Hatschek
The bible for anyone who has ever dreamed of landing a job in the music business, from producing or engineering the next Top 10 hit to running a record company. Featuring advice and secrets to educate and empower the serious music and recording industry job seeker, including: details on booming job prospects in new media, a resource directory of key publications and top industry trade organizations, interviews with pros revealing how they got their start, and networking tips.
50449505 Book...$24.95

MODERN JAZZ VOICINGS ▸ by Ted Pease and Ken Pullig
Performers and Arrangers: add color, character, and sophistication to your music. This is the definitive text used for the time-honored Chord Scales course at Berklee College of Music. Learn to use fourths, clusters, upper structure triads, and other advanced arranging and performing techniques. Includes exercises and over 80 recorded examples performed by Berklee faculty on the accompanying CD.
50449485 Book/CD $24.95

THE NEW MUSIC THERAPIST'S HANDBOOK, SECOND EDITION ▸ by Suzanne B. Hanser
Dr. Hanser's well-respected *Music Therapist's Handbook* has been thoroughly updated and revised to reflect the latest developments in the field of music therapy. Features an introduction to music therapy, new clinical applications and techniques, case studies, designing, implementing, and evaluating individualized treatment programs, and guidelines for beginning music therapists.
50449424 Book...$29.95

THE SELF-PROMOTING MUSICIAN ▸ by Peter Spellman
Take charge of your career with crucial do-it-yourself strategies. If you are an independent musician, producer, studio owner, or label, you should own this book! Features tips for writing business plans, creating press kits, using the Internet for promotion, customizing demos, and getting music played on college radio, along with a comprehensive musician's resource list.
50449423 Book...$24.95

For more information about Berklee Press
or Berklee College of Music, contact us:
1140 Boylston Street
Boston, MA 02215-3693
617-747-2146
www.berkleepress.com

As Serious About Music As You Are.
Visit your local music dealer or bookstore, or go to www.berkleepress.com

DISTRIBUTED BY